WELCOME

*I*t's up to us to save the world, and there's no time like the present. In this handbook for the eco-conscious, find out what you can do to reduce your carbon footprint, from embracing a more sustainable lifestyle – including changing your eating habits, growing your own food, going waste-free and making your home more environmentally friendly – to taking collective action and using your voice to hold politicians and companies to account.

GO GREEN

Future PLC Quay House, The Ambury, Bath, BA1 1UA

Bookazine Editorial
Editor **Philippa Grafton**
Designer **Thomas Parrett**
Senior Art Editor **Andy Downes**
Head of Art & Design **Greg Whitaker**
Editorial Director **Jon White**

Contributors
Alice Barnes-Brown, Jo Cole, Josh Croxton, Laurie Newman, Lauren Scott,
Jacqueline Snowden, Beate Sonerud, Vanessa Thorpe

Cover images
Simone Golob/Shutterstock, Getty Images

Photography
All copyrights and trademarks are recognised and respected

Advertising
Media packs are available on request
Commercial Director **Clare Dove**

International
Head of Print Licensing **Rachel Shaw**
licensing@futurenet.com
www.futurecontenthub.com

Circulation
Head of Newstrade **Tim Mathers**

Production
Head of Production **Mark Constance**
Production Project Manager **Matthew Eglinton**
Advertising Production Manager **Joanne Crosby**
Digital Editions Controller **Jason Hudson**
Production Managers **Keely Miller, Nola Cokely,
Vivienne Calvert, Fran Twentyman**

Printed by William Gibbons, 26 Planetary Road,
Willenhall, West Midlands, WV13 3XT

Distributed by Marketforce, 5 Churchill Place, Canary Wharf, London, E14 5HU
www.marketforce.co.uk Tel: 0203 787 9001

All content previously appeared in this edition of **Save The World**

Go Green First Edition (LBZ4098)
© 2021 Future Publishing Limited

Future plc is a public
company quoted on the
London Stock Exchange
(symbol: FUTR)
www.futureplc.com

Chief executive **Zillah Byng-Thorne**
Non-executive chairman **Richard Huntingford**
Chief financial officer **Penny Ladkin-Brand**

Tel +44 (0)1225 442 244

CONTENTS

Use the following articles to identify areas in your life where you can make more eco-friendly choices.

We've also busted some of the most common misconceptions about climate change and reveal the truth behind these lies. Bear these in mind in the future – you never know when you'll have to correct someone!

PART TWO:
TAKE ACTION

Images: Getty Images

CLIMATE CHANGE MYTHS BUSTED

Discover the answers to 11 of the most common misconceptions about climate change

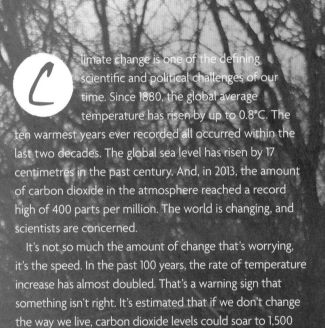

limate change is one of the defining scientific and political challenges of our time. Since 1880, the global average temperature has risen by up to 0.8°C. The ten warmest years ever recorded all occurred within the last two decades. The global sea level has risen by 17 centimetres in the past century. And, in 2013, the amount of carbon dioxide in the atmosphere reached a record high of 400 parts per million. The world is changing, and scientists are concerned.

It's not so much the amount of change that's worrying, it's the speed. In the past 100 years, the rate of temperature increase has almost doubled. That's a warning sign that something isn't right. It's estimated that if we don't change the way we live, carbon dioxide levels could soar to 1,500 parts per million over the next few hundred years. Ice will melt, sea levels will rise, weather and environments will change, and the effects could be felt for millennia.

But we haven't seen the worst of it yet, and that's the problem. Glaciers are starting to retreat, Arctic ice is thinning, and animals are already having to adapt to changes in their environment. But day-to-day life for many hasn't changed and there are still lots of questions that need to be answered.

Scientists are working to monitor the planet and to model the possible effects of changes in our climate. Satellites are pointed at the Earth, taking pictures and making measurements, and scientists on the ground are conducting studies to find out what's happening now, what happened in the past and what might happen in the future.

As this data floods in, governments are trying to take action. Taking advice from experts in the field, they are working to mitigate the risk that climate change poses to the planet. If we act now, we might be able to reverse some of the damage of human-made climate change, but the steps that need to be taken are painful, and acting before we know what's going to happen makes many feel uneasy.

The trouble is, we only have one planet. If we wait to see how the effects of climate change play out, it could be too late.

MYTH #1

"THERE'S NO GLOBAL WARMING BECAUSE THE WEATHER'S BEEN COLDER!"

These past winters, temperatures in southern Europe have plunged to double figures below freezing, and countries used to mild weather were carpeted in thick snow. Across the pond in the US, the National Oceanic and Atmospheric Association (NOAA) reported double the number of extreme snowstorms in the last half of the 20th century compared to the first. In the face of this Arctic weather, it's no wonder that climate sceptics find global warming hard to believe.

But weather isn't the same as climate. Weather is the state of the atmosphere for a short period, while climate describes what's happening long-term. The Arctic is circled by a polar vortex – circular winds that contain the chilly air. At the edges, the vortex interacts with a jet stream that brings warm air up from the equator. Normally, the worst of the winter chill is confined by this air movement, but an increase in air pressure over the Arctic, or a disruption in the jet stream, can send frigid weather southwards.

Overall, global temperatures have been rising and it's approximately a degree hotter today than it was in 1880. While fluctuations in air movement have been sending cold weather into North America, Europe and Asia, the average temperature has been climbing, hence the widespread concern.

MYTH #2

"SCIENTISTS DISAGREE ABOUT CLIMATE CHANGE"

The Earth is getting warmer; temperature records from independent organisations for more than 100 years show that the planet is heating up. The debate comes down to what's causing the rise, and climate scientists are pointing the finger at us.

Searches have been made to pull out published work referencing phrases like 'global climate change' and 'global warming'. These papers have been analysed to find out whether the scientists agree that it is happening, and about the cause. The results of seven of these independent studies were published in 2016, and together they found that between 90 and 100% of publishing climate scientists agree that global warming is caused by humans.

Backing them up are the National Academies of Science from 80 countries across the world, along with the Intergovernmental Panel on Climate Change (IPCC), a hundreds-strong team of climate experts working with the United Nations. It's hard to argue with that. Humans need to face up to their culpability, and fast.

MYTH #3

"THE CLIMATE CHANGES WE'RE SEEING TODAY ARE COMPLETELY NATURAL"

Earth has been warmer before. In fact, it's been much warmer. Geological records can reveal the state of the planet in the distant past, and during the Early Eocene Period, 54-48 million years ago, temperatures were up to 14°C higher than today. It was so hot that the ice at both poles completely melted.

Our orbit around the Sun is uneven, and as we drift closer to or further from our star, this affects our planet's climate and has been linked to the onset of ice ages. The Sun brightens from time to time, kicking out more energy, and volcanic eruptions can fill Earth's atmosphere with carbon dioxide (heating things up) or light-blocking particles (cooling things down). These factors have changed the temperature of the Earth, and will continue to affect it in the future, but that's not what's happening now.

Over the past few decades, temperatures have been rising fast. Sophisticated models of global temperature, ignoring any human input, can re-create the patterns we've observed up until the 1950s, but after that point they can't account for what's going on. Factor in the effects of the emissions humans are creating, and suddenly the models fit.

MYTH #4
"EXTREME WEATHER IS DIRECTLY CAUSED BY CLIMATE CHANGE"

There have been many more cases of extreme weather hitting the headlines over the past few years. Take the US for example, where heat waves are increasing in frequency, even in chilly states like Alaska. Winter storms are becoming more frequent and more intense and the proportion of rainfall happening in single-day flash events is increasing. Storms in the North Atlantic Ocean have also increased in intensity, frequency and duration. But it's hard to link these directly to climate change.

In 2014, NOAA published a report looking at 16 extreme weather events across the world. They found a link between human activity and heat waves, but couldn't prove that the droughts, heavy rain or storms studied were influenced by people. An increasing global temperature does increase the risk of extreme weather, and we can expect events like these to be more common in the future, but it's not yet possible to point the finger at climate change when a big storm hits.

MYTH #5

"CO₂ ISN'T THE PROBLEM, METHANE IS"

When it comes to greenhouse gases, carbon dioxide attracts the most attention. CO_2 levels in the atmosphere have been rising since the industrial revolution, but it's not the only gas responsible for global warming. Methane is 30-times better at trapping heat.

This little molecule is released when organic materials break down. It enters the atmosphere during the production and transport of fossil fuels; it leaks out as the remains of plants and animals decay; and livestock like pigs and cows release it on a daily basis. But it's not the main reason for global warming.

There's far more CO_2 in the atmosphere, and far more of it is being produced. In the US in 2014, it made up 81% of the greenhouse gas emissions, while methane accounted for just 11%. It also hangs around for hundreds, or even thousands of years, unlike methane.

MYTH #6
"MORE CO₂ IS A GOOD THING BECAUSE PLANTS NEED IT"

Carbon dioxide is a key ingredient of photosynthesis. Plants combine it with water under the power of the sunlight to create sugars, which, in turn, indirectly provide energy for pretty much every living thing on the planet. Without carbon dioxide, we wouldn't be here.

Adding more carbon dioxide to the atmosphere does boost plant growth, but in the context of climate change it's not that simple. Stanford University performed a three-year experiment to test what would happen to plant life 100 years from now if our planet keeps changing as predicted.

They doubled the carbon dioxide, raised the temperature by one degree, increased rainfall and increased soil nitrogen (an effect of fossil fuel burning). Under these combined conditions, plant growth stalled.

MYTH #7
"ANIMALS CAN ADAPT TO CLIMATE CHANGE"

Since life first emerged, Earth's temperature has fluctuated wildly. In the Eocene, it was around 14°C warmer than today, and during the last ice age, it was over four degrees colder.

Species can change their habits, move their homes or even evolve to escape climate change. For example, two-spot ladybirds can be either black with red spots, or red with black. Numbers used to be about equal, but now most are red as it seems to help keep them cool. Pink salmon are spawning earlier in warmer waters, and the quino checkerspot butterfly is moving to higher altitudes.

But these kinds of quick fixes aren't possible for every species. Climate change is happening fast, and evolution is notoriously slow. Many species are struggling to adapt to their changing world.

MYTH #8

"CLIMATE CHANGE IS A CONSPIRACY!"

This myth is the hardest to counter. Many people are automatically sceptical of any evidence climate experts might present.

Climate change isn't just about science — it's also about politics. Changing the way the world works is going to be hard, and it's no wonder that the research is meeting resistance, not least because researchers are still teasing apart the science. Our understanding is building and changing year by year.

But the truth is that internationally respected organisations like the IPCC, NASA, NOAA and the National Academies of Science from over 80 countries agree climate change is happening. The scientific consensus is that human activity is likely to be the cause. When the link between smoking and lung cancer was made, tobacco companies fought to discredit it. Now fossil fuels are in the firing line.

MYTH #9

"A FEW DEGREES WON'T MAKE ANY DIFFERENCE"

Since the late 1800s, the world has warmed by around 1°C. Sounds small, doesn't it? But a few degrees can make all the difference. Earth's story is written in its rocks, and we know that if the average temperature is just a few degrees colder we're plunged into an ice age. A few degrees warmer and the ice caps melt. The European Geosciences Union, an international union of professional Earth, planetary and space scientists, published a study in 2016 looking at the difference that half a degree could make.

An increase in carbon dioxide levels and temperature is expected to boost the growth of some crops, like soybeans and wheat, but once the temperature tips over the 1.5°C threshold, this boost could be lost. In some places, temperatures could soar by 10°C, and extreme heat and drought could cause these vital food crops to fail.

Work to unpick the consequences of the rise in temperature is still in its infancy, but using the available data, scientists in Oxford, UK have also been looking at the difference between 1.5 and 2°C. This little jump carries an increased risk of extreme weather events, like droughts, floods and storms, which could have devastating effects on populations, economies and of course the environment. Then there's sea levels. It takes a while for the oceans to catch up with the rise in atmospheric temperature, so the full impact of melting ice has yet to be seen. A couple of degrees may sound like nothing, but its impact could be huge.

MYTH #10

"CLIMATE CHANGE IS CAUSED BY THE SUN"

The Sun doesn't put out a constant stream of power. It goes through cycles of increased activity every 11 years or so, culminating in intense sunspots that rage on the surface thanks to fluctuations in its magnetic field. Over the last century, this activity has been intensifying and the Sun is brighter now than it was thousands of years ago. On top of this, Earth's orbit changes shape over time and our planet tips on its axis, changing the length and intensity of the seasons.

In the past, these cycles and changes were linked to fluctuations in temperature on Earth, including the coming and going of ice ages. But warming trends over the past few decades no longer match up to solar activity. As global temperatures have been rising, the Sun's activity has remained stable. In fact, there was a deep solar minimum between 2007 and 2009, but temperatures on Earth continued to rise.

MYTH #11

"THERE'S NOTHING WE CAN DO TO STOP CLIMATE CHANGE"

It's too early to admit defeat. We've spotted our influence on climate change early, and there's still time to intervene. The simplest way to reduce temperature-changing greenhouse emissions is to stop creating them. In 2010, a quarter came from producing electricity and heat, another quarter from agriculture and land use, around 20% from industry, and 14% from transport.

The gold standard is transitioning to renewable energy, and this is already starting to happen. In 2015, carbon dioxide emissions in the UK dropped by 4.3% thanks to a continuing drop in coal consumption. And between 2005 and 2012, emissions in the US dropped by nearly 10%.

However, with carbon dioxide levels in the atmosphere having already risen, it would take centuries for things to return to normal even if we do manage to halt our damaging activities. If we want to mitigate the greenhouse effect and halt the rise in global temperature, we need to explore other options too.

One idea is to reflect some of the sunlight back into space by seeding bright clouds over the oceans, or spraying reflective particles into the air. Another is to remove carbon dioxide from the atmosphere, either naturally by planting more trees and encouraging the growth of algae in the sea, or artificially by developing carbon sinks that can suck the gas out and store it.

PART ONE:
SUSTAINABLE LIVING

E mbracing a more environmentally friendly lifestyle goes hand in hand with sustainable living. In this section, discover ways that you can change your life right now to be better for our planet. There's so much we can improve in our day-to-day lives, from changing to a plant-based diet (page 26) and growing our own food (page 36), to ridding our lives of plastic (page 50) and upcycling old things (page 66).

Changing and breaking bad habits is another concept that we need to wrap our minds around, and one of the worst offenders in our daily lives is fast fashion. Over on page 70, find out what's so bad about it, and how we can end our addiction to clothing to improve the world around us. Travel is another addiction we face in modern-day society, and even the most vigilant eco-warriors struggle to give up these mind-expanding experiences. Instead, find out on page 98 how to take a more ece-conscious approach to holidaying, from staycationing (page 102) to being more active in our daily commutes (page 88).

Images Getty Images

GO GREEN AT HOME

We can all be a bit more mindful around our homes... and we aren't just talking about turning off lights

It can be quite overwhelming when we hear about the devastating effects that global warming is having on our planet. With the damage coming from so many causes, where on earth can we start in terms of minimising our own personal footprint? The good news is we can make a difference. We can reduce the negative impact we have on the planet by making small changes to our lifestyles from the comfort of our own homes – from switching your light bulbs to LEDs, to opting for showers over baths, there are numerous simple changes that all add up when it comes to protecting our world for future generations.

EXCELLENT NEWS! A FULLY LOADED DISHWASHER CAN ACTUALLY BE MORE WATER-EFFICIENT THAN WASHING UP BY HAND.

+ LIVE CLOSER TO WORK

Sometimes this can be easier said than done, depending on the size of the town that you live in and the field in which you work. But if you live close to work then more often than not you will live in an area where everything else you need is close to you. Not only is your commute time shorter but your carbon footprint is smaller as you are most likely to opt for walking or cycling over driving. Obviously this isn't always possible, so when commute times are greater, or you live out in the sticks but work in the city, opt for greener alternatives and choose public transport before reaching for your car keys.

+ CHOOSE GREENER ENERGY SOURCES

As consumers we have the power to decide where we want to spend our money and which companies we want to support. When it comes to choosing an energy supplier to power your home, it's important to make sure that you do your research before you settle. There are plenty of suppliers out there now that source their energy from natural and renewable sources. Depending on the company you choose, there might be a small increase in

the price you pay, but these companies are using customer money to pay for greener electricity, so even though you may notice a marginal increase in your electricity bill each month, you will be making a big difference to the planet.

If you are a homeowner you can also be conscious of where you are sourcing the energy to power your home from. For example, you could look into renewable options such as solar panels. While installing solar panels on your roof can be expensive, it can actually add value to your home and save you money on your bills in the long run. More often than not, once one person in a community makes a change like installing solar panels, it can inspire their neighbours to follow. Another way that you can make your home more green is by checking your windows and your insulation. Consider having cavity wall insulation and fitting double glazing, as these can both work wonders in the winter months by trapping in heat. This in turn reduces your energy consumption, as less is needed to maintain a consistently warm temperature in your home.

Images: Unsplash (home), Getty Images (family).

+ BE KIND TO YOUR CLOTHES AND THE PLANET

We are all aware by now of the harm that plastic is doing to our oceans, but did you know that some of that stems from simple clothes washes? When we wash our clothes, microplastics are released from the synthetics in our clothes and are frequently washed into our waterways. You can minimise this by avoiding clothes that are made out of synthetic fabrics such as polyester, and instead opting for natural fibres such as cotton. You can also reduce the amount that you are washing your clothes — obviously some items require frequent washing, but jumpers and jeans can be worn more than once before they need a wash. When you do come to wash your clothes, wash them on a lower temperature (30°C is fine for most washes) and reduce the cycle length. Although it's important to be mindful of how we are washing our clothes, it is also vital we consider how we are drying them too. Tumble dryers are one of the greediest energy

ECO EGG
The best addition to your washing routine

It's time to rethink how we are washing our clothes by switching to the Eco Egg. The Eco Egg acts as your fabric conditioner and washing powder in one by cleaning your clothes using two types of natural mineral pellets encased in a refillable egg. This innovative product is free from harmful chemicals, reduces single-use plastic, is kind to your skin and you'll save a fortune by not buying detergents. It's also

appliances in the home so avoid them as much as you can. Dry clothes on a clothes horse or outside on a washing line – it's better for the planet, and it's more gentle on your clothes as tumble dryers can be quite punishing on fabrics.

+ SWITCH UP THE BATH

Anything that requires heating up a lot of water will have a high energy consumption, so this means that you might have to reconsider your bathing routine. Endeavour to have a shower instead of a bath, as baths use a lot of water and a lot of energy. If you are someone who really enjoys baths, then see them more of a treat than a habitual way of washing.

+ A BRIGHT IDEA

We are all guilty of leaving lights on in a room that we are no longer in, but this is one of those small, easy changes

GUPPYFRIEND WASHING BAGS PREVENT MICROFIBRES ENTERING THE WATER. VISIT GUPPYFRIEND.COM

that also saves you money in the long run, so it's kind of a no-brainer! Get into the habit of switching off the lights when you leave a room and you will notice an immediate drop in your energy consumption. You can also switch over your light bulbs and opt for LEDs or any other energy-efficient bulb.

+ MINIMAL EFFORT, GREAT RESULTS

As you can see, these are all relatively simple steps that you can take inside your home to reduce your eco-anxiety and to help you feel that you too can make a difference in this climate disaster. What's even better news is that some of these changes don't even involve you having to leave your home to feel the satisfaction of knowing that you're making a positive impact!

GO GREEN, GO VEGAN

Why switching to a healthy, plant-based diet could drastically reduce your carbon footprint

egan. It's a word you've probably seen quite a lot of recently. But there's a good reason for that — if you want to cut down your emissions, going vegan is the single biggest change you can make. It's frequently been proven that a plant-based diet is far less damaging to the environment than a traditional, meaty one — and it can be much cheaper, too.

But before you decide to switch up your dinners completely, it's important to understand exactly what veganism is. Veganism means foregoing all animal products — so no more meat, dairy, fish, eggs, honey or any other animal derivatives. Instead, you'll be getting all the nutrients you need from a wide variety of fresh fruit, vegetables, nuts, seeds, grains and other plant-based products. It sounds complicated, but it's really not — a lot of the foods we consume every day (such as some breads) are naturally vegan anyway. Some foods, like dairy products and eggs, will need replacing, but never fear — thanks to the rapidly growing demand for vegan products, there are so many alternative options available to you in your local supermarket.

GOOD FOR THE PLANET, GOOD FOR YOU

Plant-based diets aren't just great for the environment — there are a number of reasons you should consider making the switch

IT'S HEALTHY

Done properly, a vegan diet will provide you with all the nutrients you need. If you reduce your consumption of meat and dairy, you'll have more room for healthier alternatives, and you might feel the difference very quickly.

IT'S KINDER

One of the main reasons people go vegan is because they no longer wish to contribute to animal cruelty. By cutting out animal products, you will no longer be supporting the slaughter or ill treatment of farm animals.

IT'S TASTIER

Changing up your diet means you will be thinking more creatively about what you eat. You can experiment with new dishes and flavours, and see it as a great opportunity to improve your culinary prowess.

+ GREAT FOR YOU, GREAT FOR MOTHER EARTH

According to Greenpeace, livestock (that's mostly cattle, pork, sheep and chickens) generates as much carbon dioxide as all cars, trucks, and other vehicles on the road combined. In fact, animal agriculture makes up nearly 15% of all the world's emissions – even more than the entire transport industry. That's because, in addition to the vast amounts of methane famously produced by cows, a lot of fossil fuels are required to raise the millions of animals humans consume every year. They require feed to be produced, transportation and a huge amount of power to keep the farm systems running smoothly. There's a surprising amount of energy that goes into your beef burger.

Plus, there's the question of land use – more than three-quarters of the world's agricultural land is taken up by activities related to animal farming. Despite this, it provides less than 20% of the world's calorie consumption. If everyone switched to a vegan diet, we could reduce our land use by 75%, thereby cutting our carbon emissions dramatically. Think of how that land could be used instead – to reforest the Amazon, for wildlife conservation, to use for green energy, or to grow even more vegan crops. The possibilities are endless.

You may also be familiar with recurrent water shortages in certain parts of the world. Water is obviously a crucial resource, and using less of it is key to living a sustainable lifestyle. Animal agriculture, on the other hand, uses vast amounts of the stuff – 1 pound of beef uses more than 6,800 litres of water, which is enough to fill more than 30 bathtubs. Other meats aren't much better either – you need around 2,000 litres of water to produce 1 pound of chicken. By contrast, soybeans (the most common vegan protein) need only around 900 litres per pound. Switching to a plant-based diet could help to mitigate the effects of drought, and helps us to conserve water for generations to come.

It's not just meat that causes problems for the environment, either. As tasty as a cheesy pizza or creamy

WHAT'S ON YOUR PLATE?

This striking bar chart shows the grams of CO_2 (and other harmful gases) emitted per gram of protein in different food types

FOOD TYPES	GREENHOUSE GAS EMISSIONS
Cattle, sheep and goats	62
Fish tanks	30
Fish trawling	26
Fish farms	12
Pork	10
Poultry	10
Dairy	9.1
Fishery	8.6
Eggs	6.8
Root vegetables	1.7
Wheat	1.2
Maize	1.2
Legumes	0.25

dessert is, the dairy they contain causes a number of problems for our planet. There are approximately 270 million dairy cows in the world today, and each one of those takes up significant amounts of land, water and food and produces emissions. For example, just one glass of milk (200ml) accounts for about 600g of carbon dioxide emissions. That's more than three times as much as oat, soya or almond milk – most of which are inexpensive, delicious and readily available in your local shop.

To be truly environmentally friendly, we must also watch out for what's going on in our oceans. It's a common misconception that fish farming isn't that bad for the environment – like land-based farms, fisheries destroy ecosystems and habitats, and produce emissions of their own. Waste from fish farms pollutes the ocean, and commercial fishing itself is highly controversial because

overfishing depletes the supply of certain fish in the water, disrupting food chains and upsetting the natural underwater world.

While it is true that plant-based products aren't completely carbon-neutral, their impact on the environment is far less than their animal equivalents. At first, all this information might seem overwhelming, but fear not – you have the power to change things. In a world where capital is key, the money in your eco-friendly pocket drives companies to change. The simple choice of regularly buying vegan alternatives reduces the demand for animal farming. Little by little, global carbon emissions should decrease. You, meanwhile, will be safe in the knowledge that you are doing your best to live a fully sustainable lifestyle. The best part? You can start right here, right now.

+SEASONAL SPECIALS

To make your plant-based diet even more environmentally friendly, be sure to eat seasonally and locally. There's plenty technology available to make it easier. Here are a few apps and websites that will help you to locate farmers' markets and work out what's in season:

SEASONS

This app lists the natural growing seasons and import seasons of hundreds of different kinds of produce, as well as markets around the world.

SEASONALFOODGUIDE.ORG

This website will tell you which produce is in season in every US state.

EATSEASONABLY.CO.UK

This site locates markets, restaurants and cafés that sell or cook with seasonal produce.

SPRING

+FRUIT
Blood oranges | Rhubarb | Elderflower
Alphonse mango | Gooseberries | Apricots

+VEGETABLES
Artichokes | Cauliflower | Celery | Asparagus | Leeks
Wild leaf garlic | Radishes | Chicory | Spinach | Peas
Jersey Royal potatoes | Purple sprouting broccoli | Rocket
Spring onion | Broad beans | Morels | Hispi cabbage

+HERBS
Rosemary | Oregano | Tarragon | Chives | Basil
Chervil | Coriander | Marjoramr | Bay | Flat-leaf parsley
Thyme | Dill

SUMMER

+FRUIT
Strawberries | Cherries | Blackcurrants | Peaches
Plums | Blackberries | Figs Rhubarb | Gooseberries
Melons | Grapes | Raspberries | Pears | Damsons
Greengages | Elderflower | Apricots | Redcurrants
Nectarines | Blueberries

+VEGETABLES
Broad beans | Courgettes | Chard | Radishes | Peas
Runner beans | Peppers | Cucumbers | Rocket
Aubergines | Asparagus | Potatoes | Borlotti beans
Fennel | Sweetcorn | Samphire | Spring onions | Tomatoes

+HERBS
Marjoram | Chives | Flat-leaf parsley | Thyme | Basil
Bay Chervil | Tarragon | Mint | Sage | Coriander | Dill
Oregano | Rosemary

AUTUMN

+FRUIT
Apples | Blueberries | Blackberries | Piel de sapo
Victoria plums | Cranberries | Grapes | Quince
Nectarines | Elderberries | FigsPears | Clementines

+VEGETABLES
Aubergines | Butternut squash | Leeks | Swede | Carrots
Celeriac | Turnips Cavolo nero | Celery | Pumpkin
Courgettes | Brussels sprouts | Fennel | Onions
Jerusalem artichokes | Parsnips | Kale | Tomatoes
Peppers | Cabbages | Radishes | Rocket | Potatoes

+HERBS
Basil | Chives | Flat-leaf parsley
Sage | Mint | Marjoram | Thyme Bay
Oregano | Rosemary

WINTER

+FRUIT
Pomegranates | Clementines | Blood oranges
Quince | Cranberries | Rhubarb

+VEGETABLES
Artichokes | Leeks | Potatoes | Brussels sprouts
Butternut squash | Cauliflower | Celeriac | Chicory
Swedes | Cavolo nero | Cabbage | Celery | Watercress
Spinach | Kale Broccoli | Turnips | Jerusalem artichokes
Parsnips | Onions

+HERBS
Bay | Rosemary | Sage

*Based on UK seasonality.
Produce elsewhere will vary

VEGAN SUBSTITUTES

Don't miss out on your favourite foods when you go vegan

Vegan cooking has never been easier, with so many alternative ingredients that you can swap out of non-vegan recipes. From ingenious egg replacement hacks to different fats that can be swapped in for butter, you'll never struggle to find something that will work for you. Likewise, there are many meat alternatives on offer, which means that you can still get all of the protein and nutrients found in meat so that you won't be lacking in iron or key B vitamins like it was once assumed. Just about every coffee shop now offers great cow milk alternatives to suit your tastes, and you won't have to miss out on comfort foods, such as pizza and mac-and-cheese, with the dairy-free alternatives out there.

✦ RED MEAT

Red meat is a source of protein, which helps to keep muscles and bones strong, as well as iron, zinc and other antioxidants to keep your immune system functioning. It also contains vitamin B12, which is needed for DNA and keeps our blood cells and nerves healthy. However, it is one of the worst foods for its environmental impact, and consumption of too much red meat has been linked to cancer, heart disease and other serious health risks.

SEITAN

Seitan is made from wheat gluten and contains a comparable amount of protein to red meat. It's a good source of iron and phosphorous, too. To make seitan taste like meat, you should season it in the same way as you would season meat.

LEGUMES

Although they don't taste like meat, legumes like black beans, pinto beans and lentils have similar nutrients. They are also a good source of protein, are rich in carbohydrates and healthy fibre, as well as being high in iron, zinc and phosphorous like red meat.

TEMPEH

Made from fermented soya beans, tempeh is a protein-rich meat substitute. Like red meat, tempeh provides iron, zinc, phosphorous and B vitamins. Tempeh can be used in stir fries instead of steak or sliced in sandwiches.

✦ WHITE MEAT

Similar to red meat, white meat is very nutritious. It is a great source of protein, niacin, phosphorous, vitamins B6 and B12, calcium, iron and zinc. 100g of chicken breast contains one third of your daily intake of B6 and 86% of niacin. Chicken, however, is one of the most consumed meats around the world, so millions of poultry birds are slaughtered every year.

TOFU

Tofu is a great source of protein, like poultry, and it contains all of the nine amino acids. Although it doesn't contain all of the same nutrients as poultry, it is a good source of iron, calcium, manganese, selenium, copper, zinc, magnesium and phosphorous.

TVP

Textured Vegetable Protein is an easy-to-use and cheap alternative and can be adapted into many different dishes to replace both red and white meat. It is made from dehydrated soy and comes in granules. It is a good source of protein as well as iron.

CAULIFLOWER

While not particularly similar, cauliflower works well sliced and fried like a chicken steak or coated in a batter for chicken-style fried cauliflower to satisfy your fried chicken craving. It's low-calorie and contains 11% of your recommended daily intake of B6.

✦ PORK

Pork is high in protein and contains many essential minerals and nutrients that promote a healthy body. Much like chicken, it contains all nine amino acids, as well as iron, phosphorous, B12, B6, selenium, niacin and zinc.

JACKFRUIT

Jackfruit is versatile and can be slow cooked in much the same way as pulled pork, and has a very similar texture. It doesn't contain much protein, but it does have essential nutrients like magnesium and copper.

✦ HONEY

Honey contains many nutrients and vitamins and is rich in antioxidants. Honey is also a healthier sweetener than proper sugar. Honey is known to lower cholesterol and manage blood pressure. Growing concerns about the bee population, however, have led people to question and cut down on their consumption of this important natural product.

MAPLE SYRUP

Maple syrup is actually healthier than honey and can be used in baking to replace sugar. It contains antioxidants, calcium and has many health benefits, including improving skin, digestion and inflammation.

GOLDEN SYRUP

Golden syrup is nowhere near as healthy as maple syrup, but it is delightfully sweet and sticky. Flavour your porridge with it or drizzle it on top of pancakes – but do so in moderation!

✦ EGGS

Eggs are used in so much in day-to-day cooking. One egg has 7g of quality protein as well as iron, vitamins and minerals. Concerns around battery farming and the killing of male chicks means vegans abstain from eggs.

AQUAFABA

This is often used to replace egg whites. When legumes are cooked their carbohydrates and proteins migrate into the cooking water and creates a liquid that is able to act very similarly to egg whites.

GROUND FLAX SEEDS

Mix one tablespoon of ground flax seeds with three tablespoons of water and leave for a few minutes. The mix becomes thick and gelatinous, sort of like an egg. Use this to replace one egg in recipes.

APPLESAUCE

Applesauce is a great substitute as it binds everything together, adds moisture and is low in fat. Use a third of a cup to replace each egg in your recipe and your sweet bakes should turn our perfectly.

✦ CHEESE

Cheese is full of protein, fat and various vitamins and nutrients like calcium, zinc, B2, B12, magnesium and phosphorous. It can be used to flavour various dishes and to bind ingredients. However, it is very high in fat.

NUTRITIONAL YEAST FLAKES

This is deactivated yeast and is either a powder or flakes. It has a cheesy flavour, so is used to make vegan cheese sauces for things like macaroni and cauliflower cheese.

VEGAN CHEESE

This often comes in slices or is grated and can be used on pizzas or in toasties and sandwiches. It doesn't melt in the same way as real cheese, but it's a pretty close replacement to the real thing.

✦ BUTTER

Butter has a very high fat content and can be used in a variety of recipes and as a key ingredient in many cakes and other baked goods. It is rich in flavour and is used as a spread to add flavour to bread, crackers and more.

OIL-BASED RECIPES

There are many cake recipes that use oil instead of butter. Cakes made with oil are lighter in texture and more moist. Use sunflower, olive, groundnut or coconut oil.

VEGAN MARGARINE

This is a great substitute, but it can make cakes a little oily and may taint the taste of buttercream in bakes. On the plus side, it is softer than butter and lower in calories.

✦ MILK

Cow's milk contains many nutrients. It is full of calcium, which is essential for your bones and blood pressure. It is controversial, however, because of the high amount of hormones and fat it has within it, as well as ethical concerns.

SOY MILK

Soy milk is thicker than other plant-based milks and has more protein, but has less calcium and nutrients. It may curdle when making coffee and other hot drinks.

ALMOND MILK

Almond milk tastes a little more watery then cow's milk, and doesn't have as much protein. However, one cup of almond milk has 56% of your daily intake of calcium.

OAT MILK

Oat milk is a tasty, nutrient-rich substitute, containing more than ten times the calcium than soy milk and has more protein than almond milk. It's a great milk for hot drinks.

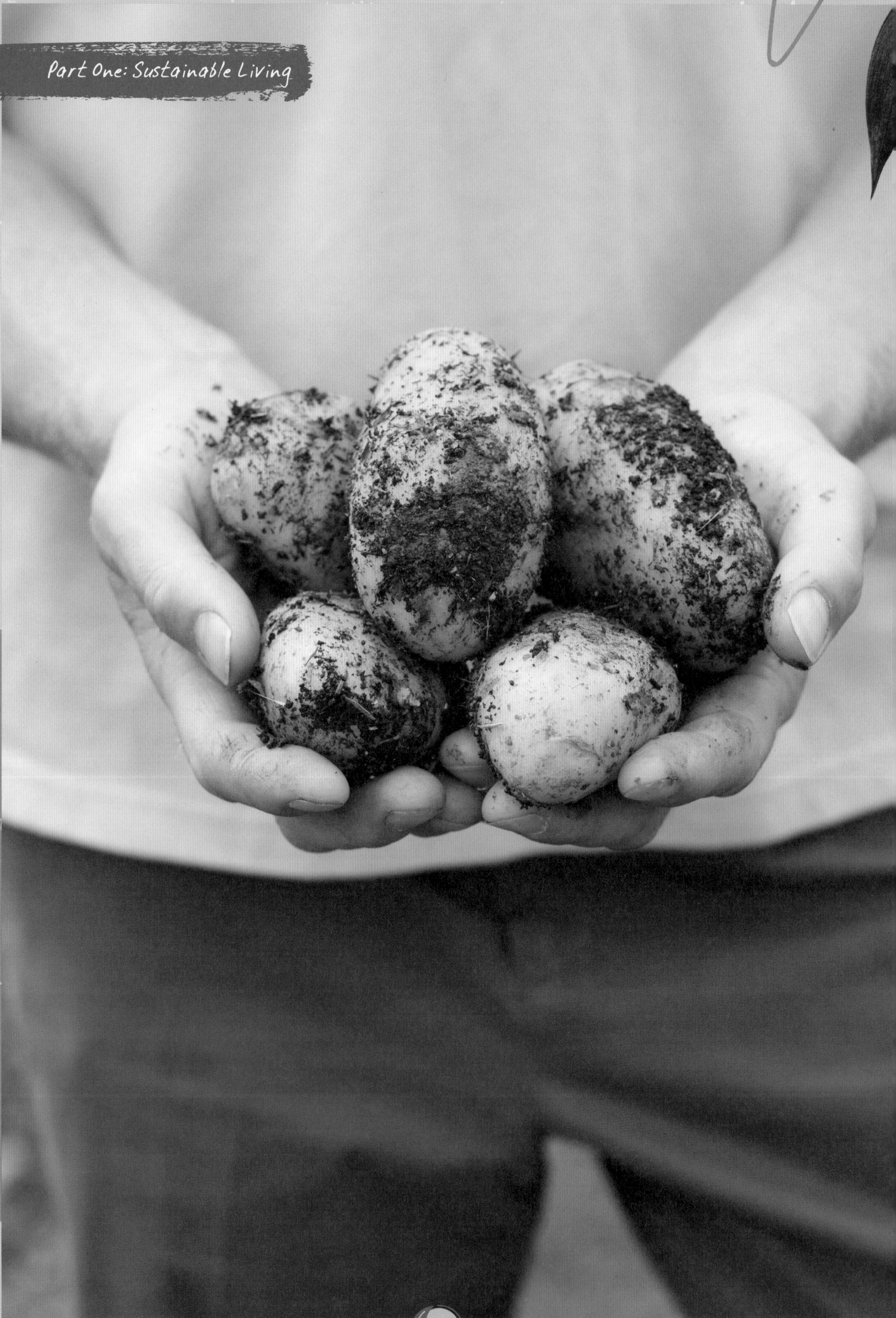

GROW YOUR OWN

Live the good life by turning your back on packaged produce and growing the most delicious fruit and veg you've ever tasted

When it comes to living a sustainable and environmentally friendly life, one area worth exploring is growing your own fruit and vegetables. Most produce in supermarkets will have done a serious amount of travelling to get to the shelves — contributing to carbon emissions — and usually have lots of plastic packaging. Unless you buy organic, it might also have been treated with pesticides or chemical fertilisers. Growing your own avoids all of that. Also, many edibles produce flowers to attract pollinators, so you are providing food for these essential buzzers as well as yourself.

Most fruit and vegetables are easy to grow, especially if you buy baby plants from a nursery. If you can put a plant in some dirt and operate a watering can, you have the skills to grow food! Not only is it an environmentally friendly activity, but picking and cooking something you have grown is one of the best feelings in the world.

Providing you have access to sunlight, you can grow food in any kind of space. Only have room for a flowerbed in your garden? Embrace the cottage garden ethos and pop vegetables in amongst the flowers. Living with a balcony? Pretty much any edible can be grown in a container. And don't feel despondent if you just have a window box or windowsill. Concentrate on herbs, dwarf varieties of plants, or explore the world of microgreens.

We're going to give you ideas of what to grow where, but the best way to find out what works is to simply to have a go. There will be disasters, but there will be many more wins!

+ ALLOTMENT OR GARDENS

If you have access to a garden or allotment, the growing world is your oyster. Dig over the area and weed it as best you can before breaking up any big clumps of soil and digging in some peat-free compost to improve its condition. If you have heavy clay soil, the compost will also help break down the structure. Next, level out the soil and add a further layer of compost.

Alternatively, you can grow in raised beds. Fill the beds with a peat-free compost and get ready to grow! You can buy beds in a variety of sizes, or make them using recycled composite decking boards. They'll last for absolutely ages. With a garden, you can grow larger produce such as

cauliflowers, sweetcorn or, as we show here, potatoes. Try different varieties and if you have the space, grow earlies, second earlies and main crop potatoes, so you can harvest these delicious dumplings for as long as possible.

GROW EARLY POTATOES

WHAT YOU'LL NEED

SPADE | FORK | SEED POTATOES
EGG CARTON | PEAT-FREE COMPOST

1. CHIT THE POTATOES

Buy early seed potatoes in late January. Place in an egg box with the eyes (the dark dents) facing upwards. Put in a light place for about six weeks. Wait until the shoots are about 2cm long.

2. MAKE A TRENCH

Dig a trench about 15cm deep, piling the soil on either side. Add some organic general purpose fertiliser and plant each seed potato with the shoots facing upwards, about 30cm apart. Gently cover with soil.

3. BURY THE TOPS

Green shoots will appear. When they're about 20cm high, build up soil around them, leaving about 5cm at the top. This is called 'earthing up'. Keep the crop watered.

4. AND REPEAT

Continue this burying process. Because these are earlies, repeat until the flowers open (usually the start of June). If you planted a main crop, wait for the stems to wither.

5. DIG FOR TREASURE

To harvest, gently dig away some soil to check there are some ready to dig up. If you're in luck, use a fork to gingerly lift up the potatoes.

LIVING WITH PLASTIC

Get creative with container ideas to minimise the plastic you use

Gardening can involve a lot of plastic – from compost bags to plant pots or seed trays – so don't buy more than is necessary.

Reuse existing containers. As long as something has drainage holes, it can be used to plant in. Look out on Freecycle for old buckets, sinks, troughs or builders' bags. Someone might even be offering plastic plant pots – if you can use them, take them. It's better than them ending up on landfill and they will last for years.

Tomatoes are an excellent edible to embark on container growing. There are so many types suitable for pots and the plants can easily be picked up at garden centres. Here's how it's done.

GROW TOMATOES
WHAT YOU'LL NEED

**CONTAINER (AT LEAST 30CM DIAMETER) OR GROW BAG
PEAT-FREE COMPOST | TROWEL
CANE | TWINE | TOMATO FOOD**

1. GET IN POSITION
Fill your container with peat-free compost, dig a hole and plant one tomato plant. Ensure about two-thirds of the stem is covered. Use three canes to make a pyramid shape and secure with twine.

2. TIE AND TRIM
As the plants grow, gently tie them to the cane with twine. Keep an eye out for any side shoots emerging between leaves and the main stem. If you see any, pinch them out.

3. WATER REGULARLY
It's important that you water tomato plants regularly and increase frequency if the weather is very hot. Erratic watering will cause tomatoes to split.

4. FEED THE FRUIT
Once you see flowers appear, feed with tomato food every couple of weeks and carry on doing this right through the growing season.

5. CUT BACK AND HARVEST
To pick a tomato, place your thumb on the 'knuckle' above the stem and lift up. As you get to the end of the season, cut back excessive leaves so the sun can ripen the last of the fruit.

+ ON A BALCONY OR IN A WINDOW BOX

Plants are tough. If given soil, water, light and feed, they'll make a go at growing pretty much anywhere. Never feel as though you are at a disadvantage if you can only use containers on a balcony – you'll still be able to grow your own food, it just might be on a reduced scale. In fact, the main issue you'll face when growing on a balcony is keeping an eye on weight. Big containers of soil can get incredibly heavy, so make sure your balcony can support the heft!

As long as the container is big enough, you can grow potatoes, cabbages, cauliflower, carrots, beetroot... pretty much anything you can think of. You can also think vertically. Hanging baskets or window boxes are perfectly adequate for small varieties of raspberries, strawberries, herbs, salad leaves, radishes, or else anything with a short root system. Just be vigilant when it comes to watering and feeding. Containers can dry out quickly and plants will soon gobble up any nutrients in the compost, so be sure to feed and water regularly.

+ON AN INDOOR WINDOWSILL

Okay, so you can't grow enough edibles on a windowsill to become self-sufficient, but you can still get a surprising amount of produce. Providing the container you use is deep enough and you get a decent amount of sunlight, you can grow anything from baby carrots to beetroot, tomatoes or strawberries. Look out for dwarf varieties of fruit and vegetables and just see what works!

Salad leaves are particularly good for windowsills and you can sow directly into your container from seed. There is a huge choice of varieties and with a bit of planning you can have leaves all year round. Look at the back of the seed packet for instructions on when to sow and when you can expect to harvest.

Herbs are great produce to grow on a windowsill and most are very happy living in pots. You can pick up herb plants from nurseries or supermarkets; just pop them on a saucer and you're ready to go. Basil is excellent to start with – it's easy to grow and tastes delicious. Here's what's involved...

GROW BASIL
WHAT YOU'LL NEED

**BASIL PLANT | POT
PEAT-FREE COMPOST**

1. GET IN PLACE
Repot your basil if needed and then position on a sunny windowsill. Basil is a Mediterranean herb, so it needs sunlight. Rotate it regularly to encourage even growth.

2. WATER SPARINGLY
You don't need to flood basil with water. Wait until the soil is dry and then water until it comes out the holes at the bottom of the pot. Tip this away so the basil isn't sitting in water.

3. PINCH THE TIPS
Encourage the basil to be as bushy as possible by pinching out the small leaves from the top of a stalk to promote sideways growth.

4. SUMMER BOLT
If it gets hot, basil can shoot up and try to flower (bolt). Snip the flowers off, as well as a few leaves below the flower, to prevent this.

GROW COURGETTES

WHAT YOU'LL NEED

**SPADE | CARDBOARD OR STRAW | KNIFE
PEAT-FREE COMPOST | EGG CARTON**

1. DIG A HOLE

We're using an allotment/garden scenario here, but you can also grow courgettes in pots. Use one plant per (large) container. In the ground, dig a hole about 10cm deep and wide, add some compost and then plant.

2. SPACE AND WATER

Leave about a metre between each plant, because they grow very, very large. Once planted, give them a water but avoid getting the leaves soaked as it can cause mildew.

3. PROTECT THE COURGETTES

When all the plants are in the ground, put some cardboard or straw at the base of the plants. This is to keep the courgettes off the ground so they don't go rotten.

BUY YOUNG COURGETTE PLANTS IN SPRING AND PLANT IN LATE MAY/EARLY JUNE WHEN THERE'S NO RISK OF FROST

4. WATER REGIME

Courgettes like water, so don't let them dry out. When you notice the fruits appear, feed with a high potash liquid fertiliser every ten days. Continue during the growing season.

5. PICK 'EM QUICK!

When the courgettes are at a size you like, use a sharp knife to lop them off where the fruit joins the stem. Keep picking, otherwise it'll feel like you're buried under marrows.

COOK YOUR OWN PRODUCE

Cooking with produce that you have grown is a wondrous thing. Yes, you can be happy in the fact your food has no pesticides, chemical fertilisers or wasteful plastic associated with it, but more than anything, it tastes so good! Simple recipes are absolutely the best way to go. You don't want to disguise the taste of your produce, so make it the star of the dish. Use the recipes here to get started and please feel free to swap ingredients to add more of what you like (or what has grown!) or play around with the measurements.

+ CHUNKY TOMATO SAUCE

A simple, but super-tasty dish

WHAT YOU'LL NEED

250G TOMATOES
1 ONION
1 CLOVE OF GARLIC, CRUSHED
1 RED PEPPER
1 TBSP OLIVE OIL

1. Gather your tomatoes and pierce with a knife. Slice the onion and pepper.

2. Heat the oil in a frying pan over a medium heat and add the tomatoes, onion, garlic and pepper.

3. Cook until the tomatoes are soft, then use the back of a spoon to squash down into the pan.

4. Continue to cook for a few more minutes, stirring everything together.

5. For a pasta sauce, stir in a little pasta water to make the sauce silky. Or why not toast some sourdough bread and slather with the tomato sauce?

+ MEDITERRANEAN EARLY POTATOES

A one-tray side-dish to showcase your potatoes

WHAT YOU'LL NEED

500G EARLY POTATOES
1 TBSP OLIVE OIL
2 CLOVES OF GARLIC, CHOPPED
1 TSP CHOPPED LEMON THYME
1 ONION | 2 LEMONS
SALT AND PEPPER TO TASTE

1. Preheat the oven to 200°C (390°F), gas mark 6.

2. Wash the potatoes and cut any larger ones in half – they all need to be roughly the same size.

3. Cut the onion and lemon into wedges and put into a bowl, along with the potatoes, oil, garlic and lemon thyme. Add salt and pepper to taste.

4. Toss everything around, spread onto a baking tray and put in the oven for around 30 minutes, or until the potatoes are soft.

+ BASIL OIL

A subtle basil taste to complement all kinds of food

1. Wash the basil leaves, then pop them in a pan of boiling water for a minute.

2. Take the leaves out of the boiling water and immediately put them into a bowl of iced water.

3. Squeeze the leaves dry, then put them in a blender along with the oil and a pinch of salt.

4. Blitz until the basil is in tiny bits.

5. Decant to a container to use immediately, or keep in the fridge for about a week. Use it on everything!

WHAT YOU'LL NEED

2 HANDFULS OF BASIL LEAVES
250ML EXTRA VIRGIN OLIVE OIL
PINCH OF SALT
BOWL OF ICED WATER

WASTE-FREE KITCHEN

With a little planning and some simple swaps, you can learn to love leftovers and ditch disposable products

T he kitchen is the heart of the home, but it's also where we can be the most wasteful. Forgotten fruit, piles of peelings and a slew of single-use plastics, they all add up. It can often feel as though you're fighting a losing battle against waste, but fear not! There are plenty of ways you can curb the amount of produce and packaging that ends up in the bin.

+ 'COMPLEAT' YOUR FOOD

We often end up throwing out perfectly edible parts of our food, like skins, leaves and stalks. Challenge yourself to use up as much of these neglected ingredients as possible, and you might be surprised at the impact 'compleating' has on your usual food waste production.

Do you really need to peel your spuds and carrots? For many people, it's just a force of habit or a visual preference, but it both creates waste and robs us of a great source of fibre and vitamins. Try just giving your veg a good scrub when you wash them instead. Not only will this save you time, it will remove any tough bits while keeping lots of nutritious roughage intact.

If you don't want to include potato skins in your mash (although give it a try), turn the peel into a tasty snack by coating them in a little oil, seasoning and baking in the oven until crispy. You can make crisps with lots of other veg, or fruits like apple and pear skins too. For fruit crisps, skip the oil and seasoning and add some cinnamon instead. For more tips, search for 'compleating' online.

COMPOSTING FOOD WASTE

Let microbes work their magic to give your food scraps a second life as eco-friendly fertiliser

Find a sheltered, shady spot and start your compost heap over bare earth, with a loose cover over it to keep the warmth in, or invest in a dedicated compost bin. Fruit and vegetable scraps can go on the heap, as well as other compostable items such as eggshells, plastic-free tea bags and garden waste like grass clippings and weeds. Don't compost meat or dairy products though, as this can attract pests. Turn the compost every month or so to keep it aerated, and it should be ready to use on your garden after about six months.

+ USING UP LEFTOVERS

When a recipe calls for half of this or a handful of that, we're often left with ingredients that can easily go to waste. Plan meals in advance to identify which dishes will create leftovers so you can figure out how to use them up later in the week. Websites like **lovefoodhatewaste.com** can help you find recipes based on what you've got available.

Avoid food being forgotten by keeping your fridge and cupboards well organised. Store items that need to be used up first towards the front, or on their own shelf, so they're easily visible.

FREEZING FRUIT & VEG

Don't waste fresh produce — extend its lifespan with the help of your freezer

- You can freeze fruit and veg whole, but it is often easier to prepare them in the way you are most likely to use them — sliced carrots, potato wedges or hulled strawberries, for example — and to remove stones from fruits like cherries or plums.
- Most fruits, onions and peppers can be frozen raw. Wash them well and dry thoroughly by patting with a clean tea towel.
- Most other vegetables will keep better if blanched first. Briefly submerge them in boiling water (for 2-5 minutes), and then immediately transfer to a bowl of ice water to cool. Drain and dry them thoroughly.
- Spread the produce in a single layer on a freezer-safe tray and freeze for 4-6 hours, or until solid. Transfer the fruit/veg into a sealable freezer container or bag (remove as much air as possible), label with the contents and date, and return to the freezer.
- Most fruit and veg will keep in the freezer for 8-12 months, but citrus fruit should be used within three months.

+ DECIPHERING DATES

Another factor that contributes to a lot of food waste is the common confusion between the different types of dates printed on food packaging. We naturally tend to err on the side of caution, but lots of perfectly good food ends up in the dustbin because we don't know our 'best before's from our 'use by's.

'Sell by' and 'display until' dates are for retailers, and these don't indicate when an item needs to be eaten by. 'Best before' dates relate to quality, but not safety, so food will be fine to eat (if stored correctly) for a few days beyond this date. Use your senses to judge whether something is still edible — if something has gone off you will most likely be able to tell by sight, by giving it a sniff, or by tasting a small amount of it.

The most important dates to pay attention to are 'use by's. These are often listed on foods that go off quickly and could pose a health risk if eaten after the specified date, even if they look or smell fine. These dates are also dependent on the product being stored correctly, so make sure you pay attention to whether something needs to be refrigerated or eaten within a few days of opening.

Don't beat yourself up if you miss a few 'use by' dates or find the occasional mouldy apple — you can still make sure out-of-date food goes to good use. Food waste collections are now common across the UK, where it is composted to produce energy and fertiliser. If you have a garden or allotment, you could also try using food scraps to make your own compost.

+ BATCH COOKING

Invest time in planning and preparation and you can make your own ready meals to freeze and enjoy another time. Not only will this help you avoid the plastic packaging of shop-bought microwave meals, it'll most likely save you time and money too!

Meals with sauces freeze well, so things like stews, curries, soups and chilli are a good place to start. Plan what you want to make for the week ahead and buy enough ingredients to cook double the portions you usually serve. So, if you usually cook for two, make enough for four and freeze the extra portions. By the end of the week you'll have another week's worth of meals in the freezer, ready and waiting for a day when you don't have time to cook.

Alternatively, you can dedicate a few hours at the weekend to cooking up lots of meals for the week ahead. Freeze and label all the portions, then simply defrost each one as and when you need it, either in the fridge overnight or in the morning before you go to work.

You may need to buy a set of freezable and microwavable containers (see 'Storage options' on page 58), but some plastic takeaway containers are freezer-safe so be sure to reuse them.

+ USE YOUR FREEZER

If you have a freezer, it can become your new ally in the fight against kitchen waste. If there's anything freezer-friendly you're not going to use while it's still in date, make sure you freeze it straight away to keep it fresh. Most meat and produce freeze well if properly prepared (see below for freezing tips), but items with a high water content – such as cucumbers and salad leaves – will go soggy when they thaw.

Always make sure you label what you freeze with both the contents and the date. Find out how long different foods can be frozen for by heading to:

foodsafety.gov/food-safety-charts/cold-food-storage-charts

GOING PACKAGING-FREE

The fight against waste can now start even before you bring your groceries home

Do some research into what your local shops offer in terms of sustainable packaging and in-store recycling. A few supermarkets are trialling 'bring your own container' schemes at deli counters and, in some cases, dedicated refill stations for items like cereals, rice and pasta.

One great way to find plastic- and packaging-free food is at farmers' markets. You can take your own bags and containers, support local producers and reduce the food miles of your shop.

+ DITCHING DISPOSABLES

Paper towels, cling film and tin foil are just some of the many single-use items that fill our kitchen bins, but now there are a whole range of reusable alternatives on the market that can replace our regular disposables. See 'Reusable products', right, for some suggested swaps you can make.

While they may initially be more expensive, reusable items will often pay for themselves within a few uses. Regardless, the initial cost will be worth it when you see just how much impact these swaps have on reducing your kitchen waste.

It may take a little getting used to, but in the same way that we quickly adapted to bringing our own bags to the supermarket, it will soon become second nature.

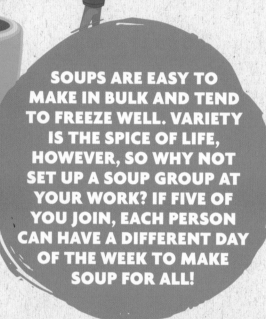

SOUPS ARE EASY TO MAKE IN BULK AND TEND TO FREEZE WELL. VARIETY IS THE SPICE OF LIFE, HOWEVER, SO WHY NOT SET UP A SOUP GROUP AT YOUR WORK? IF FIVE OF YOU JOIN, EACH PERSON CAN HAVE A DIFFERENT DAY OF THE WEEK TO MAKE SOUP FOR ALL!

STORAGE OPTIONS

Having plenty of containers on hand for your leftovers is key to any waste-free kitchen

Sealable tubs are a convenient way to store leftovers for tomorrow's lunch or freeze portions for another time. Look for freezer- and microwave-safe tubs in a variety of sizes with good seals – this keeps the air out so your food stays fresh for longer, and also helps prevent leaks.

If you're avoiding plastic, consider glass or stainless steel tubs. But remember: when storing food you plan to reheat, you can't put stainless steel containers in the microwave!

+ YOUR WASTE-FREE JOURNEY

The changes discussed here may seem a bit overwhelming at first, and will likely require some adjustments to your usual shopping and cooking routines. The important thing is to work on the aspects that are most relevant and achievable for you. If you don't have a freezer, for example, then batch cooking won't be the most practical thing to focus on, but swapping single-use items for reusable alternatives is something we can all work towards.

It will take time to incorporate these changes into your kitchen habits, but remember that going waste-free is a marathon, not a sprint. Chart your progress on the next page to see just how far you've come.

CIRCULAR CONSUMPTION

Circular consumption patterns allow us to use products without the negative side-effect of waste

More than 2.1 billion tons of waste are generated globally each year. Those of us living in developed economies with a high level of consumption contribute disproportionally to this growing mass of waste: In the US, a massive 773kg of waste is generated per person every year, more than three times as much as a Chinese citizen, and seven times more than the average Ethiopian.

If we bought less, we would waste less, you may think. But solving the waste problem by curbing consumption is not a viable strategy: Over the next decades, globally we will be consuming more, not less, as the world population grows and incomes in developing economies continue to rise.

Instead of limiting consumption, we need to change the way that we actually consume things so that we can use products without generating waste at the end. Currently, we typically extract natural resources to make stuff, then use that stuff for only a short time before throwing it away. A circular model of consumption, on the other hand, would keep all materials in a loop: when we are done with a product, the materials would be reused or recycled.

While circularity, and recycling in particular, isn't a new concept, globally only 16% of waste is recycled today. Even many developed economies struggle to make recycling mainstream: In Germany, the recycling rate is 68%, but in the UK it's only 44%, and in the US, it drops to 26%.

We need businesses and governments to implement a

circular model of production and consumption – one that includes recycling, but also goes beyond it, to design products for repair and reuse. But as consumers, we can already increase the circularity of our consumption to better deal with our waste, across everything from food and packaging to clothes and electronics.

✦ WHAT TO DO WITH FOOD

For food waste, we can choose home composting or food waste collection through local authorities, or a combination of the two. For those living in urban environments, home composting may not be an option. However, many local authorities will

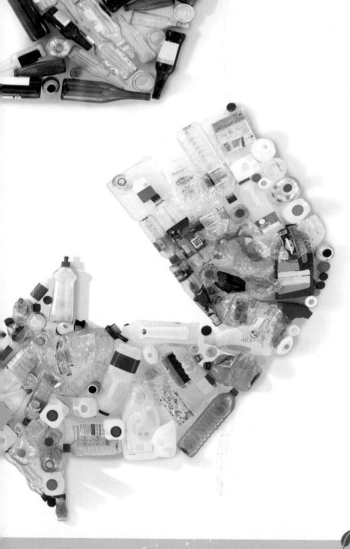

collect food waste in separate bins and take it to be commercially composed, or treated through anaerobic digestion, a process that produces green electricity.

But before dismissing your surplus food as waste in the first place, consider whether someone else might be able to use it. Various apps now enable you to share superfluous food within local communities. For example, OLIO connects neighbours with each other and with local businesses, enabling whoever has excess food to share it with someone who wants it instead of wasting it.

✦ WHAT TO DO WITH PACKAGING

For packaging, recycling logos on each item of packaging tells us whether the item is recyclable or not. Checking local recycling guidelines is also necessary, as it varies from place to place – also within countries – which items are considered recyclable. In the UK for example, every local authority has slightly different rules and practices around waste and recycling. A general rule for recycling packaging, though, is to get rid of any food or drink residue before recycling.

Supermarkets also often offer additional recycling services, for example for plastic bags. In some countries, including Norway and Sweden, consumers are even incentivised to bring their plastic bottles and cans back to supermarkets for recycling through a deposit scheme that gives consumers money back when they return bottles and cans.

✦ WHAT TO DO WITH CLOTHING AND ELECTRONICS WASTE

Unwanted clothes or electronics that are still of reasonable quality can be sold online, so-called 'recommerce'. As with surplus food, someone else might still find a use for what you consider waste. A huge number of websites (eBay, Gumtree etc) offer a marketplace for second-hand products. There are also sector-specific websites, like thredUP, the world's largest thrift store for second-hand clothing. Freecycle is another option, if you are happy to give away your stuff for free.

Several retailers also now have trade-in schemes for used products that typically

you. Global clothing brand H&M have collection points in most of their stores, where they accept used clothes regardless of brand and condition. They will sort which clothes can go to second-hand stores and which are only suitable for recycling – and they give you a voucher for money off your next purchase per bag of used textiles you hand in.

Alternatively, worn-out clothes and electronics can also be dropped off at product-specific recycling points, often located by supermarkets or local car parks.

✦ GO FURTHER: BUY PRODUCTS DESIGNED FOR CIRCULARITY

How much of our waste can be reused or recycled will depend on which products we choose to buy in the first place. Some packaging, clothing and electronics is designed for maximum repairability, reuseability and recyclability at their end of life, while others are not. Considering these aspects of a product at the purchasing stage will mean a smaller share of the products we use have to end up as waste, and instead the materials can be used over and over again with ease. As consumers, it's in our power to choose to buy products from the companies that are leading the way in designing out waste from products (see below).

offer you some form of financial reward. With online retailer Amazon's Trade In programme, you declare the condition of your item, Amazon will make an offer, and if you accept and return the item to them, they credit you with an Amazon eGift card for the agreed amount. Technology giant Apple offers a similar scheme, both in-store and online, and if the device you want to get rid of doesn't have a trade-in value, they will recycle it for

COMPANIES DESIGNING OUT WASTE

PACKAGING

A group of large brands, retailers and packaging companies have committed to working towards using 100% reusable, recyclable or compostable packaging by 2025 or earlier, including Amcor, Colgate-Palmolive, Ecover, evian, L'Oréal, Mars, M&S, Nestle, PepsiCo, the Coca-Cola Company, Unilever, Walmart and Werner & Mertz.

CLOTHING

H&M aims to go fully circular by changing design, material choices, production processes and product use, as well as product reuse and recycling. Outdoor retailer Patagonia aims to repair and reuse as many products as possible, and recycle 100% of the rest.

ELETRONICS

Fairphone is a smart-phone with modular design that allows you to customise, upgrade and repair the phone rather than simply buying a new one. At the end of its life, the phone is also designed to be easily recyclable. Larger companies, including Apple, Google and Samsung, are also increasing recycling and the use of recycled and renewable materials in their products.

RECYCLING SYMBOLS

A universal language, recycling symbols tell us which bin to put our rubbish in – but do you know what they mean?

✦ MOBIUS LOOP

The Mobius Loop is arguably the most common and widely recognised recycling symbol in the world. Created for an art competition to celebrate the first Earth Day in 1970, the symbol is usually depicted in black, green or as an outline. The symbol means the item can be recycled, as opposed to being made of recycled materials.

✦ WIDELY RECYCLED

This means the packaging can be recycled by more than 75% of local authorities in the UK. Sometimes other instructions are included, such as 'Rinse' (to reduce the risk of attracting vermin), 'Lid/Cap on' (to stop small parts falling through holes during the sorting process), 'Flatten' (to reduce space), and 'Remove Sleeve' (if it's not recyclable).

✦ RECYCLABLE ALUMINUM

This logo means the item is made of recycled aluminum. As well as foil, you'll find it on drink cans, screw-top lids, takeaway containers and roasting trays. If you're presented with a shiny wrapper and can't find the logo just scrunch it into a ball – if it stays scrunched it's aluminum foil, if it springs open it's not.

✦ CHECK LOCALLY

The white circular arrow on a black square means that only 20% to 70% of local authorities in the UK are equipped to recycle this form of material, usually a type of plastic. In this case it's best to look on your local council's website or contact the waste department for clarification.

✦ NOT YET RECYCLED

Disappointingly this logo (which is the same as 'Check Locally' but with a diagonal line crossed through it), means the product is currently only recycled by fewer than 20% of local authorities in the UK. This symbol often appears on items like foil wrapping paper, bouquet film and crisp packets.

✦ THE GREEN DOT

Commonly thought to mean the item is recyclable, this logo, showing two interlocking arrows that form a circle (sometimes in black and white, other times in light and dark green), actually means the manufacturer has paid a financial contribution to recycling services in Europe and isn't necessarily recyclable or made of recycled materials.

THE CHALLENGE OF RECYCLING
What do those numbers on your plastics mean?

△ PET
POLYETHYLENE TEREPHTHALATE
Bottles, food jars, clothing, carpet fibre, some shampoo and mouthwash bottles

△ HDPE
HIGH-DENSITY POLYETHYLENE
Detergent and bleach bottles, snack boxes, milk jugs, toys, buckets, plant pots and bins

△ PVC
POLYVINYL CHLORIDE
Credit cards, window and doorframes, gutters, pipes and synthetic leather

△ LDPE
LOW-DENSITY POLYETHYLENEE
Bottles, food jars, clothing, carpet fibre, some shampoo and mouthwash bottles

△ PP
POLYPROPYLENE
Bottle tops, drinking straws, lunch boxes, coolers, fabric and carpet fibres, tarps and nappies

△ PS
POLYSTYRENE
Plastic-foam cups, egg boxes, meat trays, packing peanuts, coat hangers, yoghurt pots and insulation

△ OTHER
Nylon fabrics, baby bottles, compact discs, medical storage containers, car parts and watercooler bottles

KEY – RECYCLABLE?
△ **EASY**
△ **MANAGEABLE**
△ **DIFFICULT**
▲ **VERY DIFFICULT**

✦ GLASS

This illustration explains that the packaging is made of glass and should be disposed of at a bottle bank – remembering to separate colours, of course – or to use your council's household glass collection service.

THE PLASTIC PROBLEM

Plastic waste is choking the planet. What can we do to clean the trash from the oceans?

Somewhere between Hawaii and California, a vast inflatable coastline swept through the sea. Beneath a 600-metre-long float, a three-metre deep skirt raked the ocean. Forced along by wind and waves, it moved faster than the currents, bending as it travelled to form a U-shaped net. Fish dived beneath to escape its advances, but as the system roamed the water it gathered a strange catch. Braving gales and storms and resisting the corrosive effects of sea salt, System 001 sent signals to satellites overhead and boats close by to collect a haul unlike any other. This net trawled the Great Pacific Garbage Patch, and its job was to clean up the sea.

The Pacific Garbage Patch is a trash vortex; a swirling gyre of waste caught up in ocean currents. While not the literal island of rubbish described in the media, its waters are strewn with small chunks of floating debris. Churned by the action of the waves, the pieces bob up and down in the water column, circulating with the currents. Invasive species hitch a ride on the travelling plastics, making their way to waters nature never intended for their occupation. Sea birds, marine mammals and fish mistake the floating chunks for food, filling their bellies with indigestible trash. The pieces that remain wear away under the relentless rocking, rubbing microscopic plastic splinters and toxic chemicals into the water.

Deployed for its first campaign on 16 October 2018 and returning to shore on 17 January 2019, System 001 aims to clear half of the rubbish from the Pacific Garbage Patch over the next five years. It is the first of a network of 60, and the result of more than 270 scale model tests and six prototypes. Pushed along by natural forces and equipped with solar-powered electronics, System 001 quietly follows the flow of the water. It's got lights and GPS to warn sailors, and it moves slowly enough that fish have plenty of time to get out of the way. Plastic, on the other hand, can't escape: trapped between the inflatable float and the solid skirt, it has nowhere to go. Load by load, sea-going rubbish trucks will retrieve the waste and start to clear the ocean. If all goes well, the project could roll out across the globe to remove 90% of our floating junk by 2040.

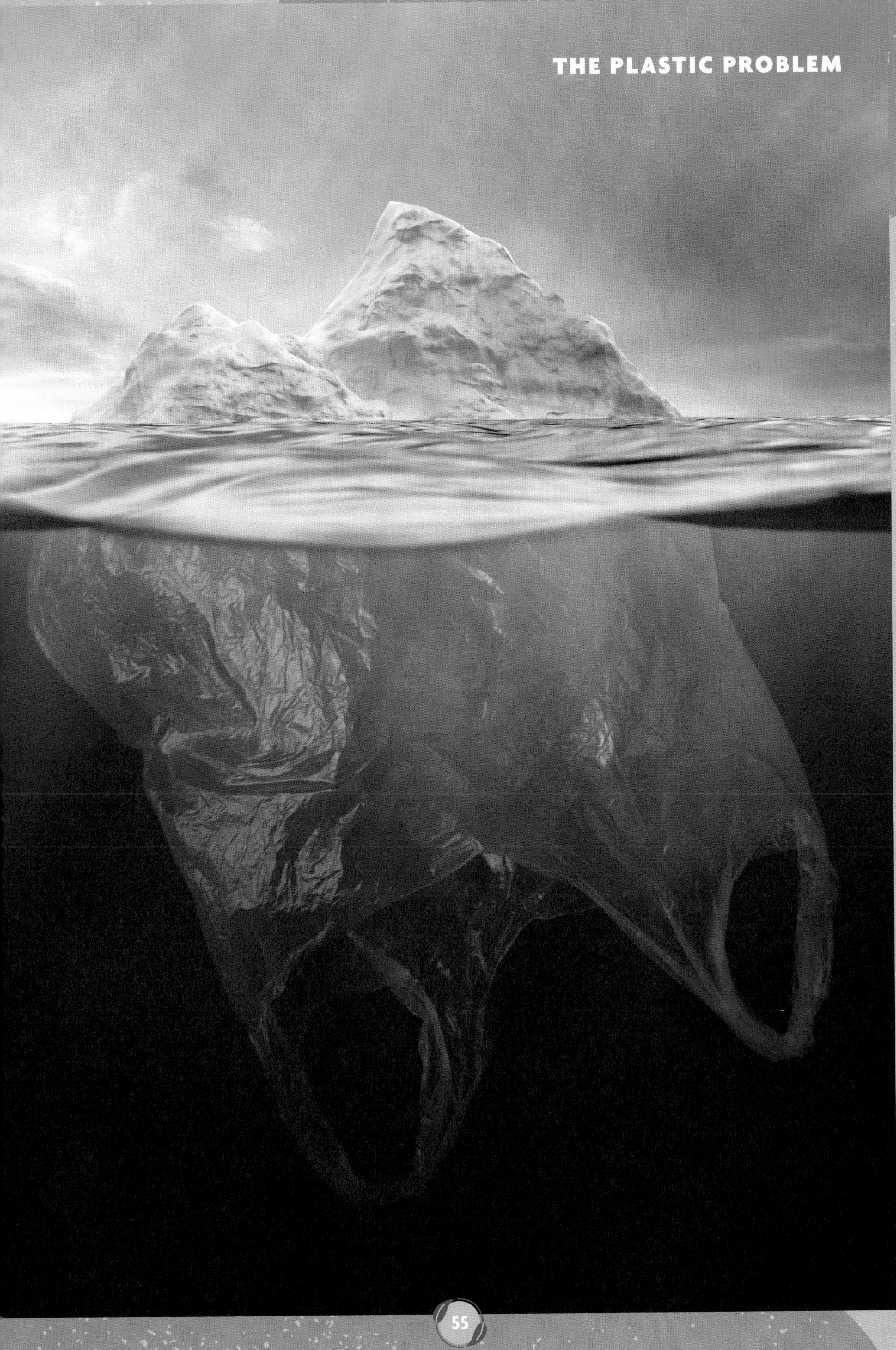

Image Getty Images

WHAT IS PLASTIC?

Plastic polymers are chains of molecules linked by carbon-carbon bonds.

Polymer chains contain thousands of repeating subunits called monomers.

Polymers also exist in nature, but their chemical bonds break down more easily.

Thermo-plastics melt when they get hot, reforming into new shapes.

Thermosets fix into one shape and don't melt when heated.

Chemical additives, like dyes, can slot between the polymer chains.

There are seven kinds of plastic, sorted according to their chemical similarities.

The raw ingredients for plastics are hydro-carbons from coal, gas and oil.

HOW DOES PLASTIC GET OUT?

CONSTANT CONSUMPTION

The world produces 300 million tons of plastic each year, half of which we use just once before discarding it.

CONTAMINATED WATER

Over 110,000 tons of microplastics wash over agricultural land in North America and Europe every single year.

MICROPLASTIC SOUP

There are more than 5 trillion pieces of plastic floating about in the oceans.

PLASTIC PER PERSON

The average person in the EU makes 31kg of plastic waste every year.

IN THE LAUNDRY

Acrylic clothes release over 700,000 plastic fibres per 6kg wash. Polyester releases nearly 500,000.

RIVERS OF RUBBISH

Our rivers carry around 100,000 rubbish trucks' worth of plastic waste out to sea each year.

+ HOW DID WE GET HERE?

It's barely more than 100 years since Leo Baekeland invented the first fully synthetic plastic. Developed to insulate electrical wires at the tail end of the second industrial revolution, this new material was unlike anything seen before. Cheap to produce, resistant to heat and highly mouldable, it could be anything people wanted it to be, and its appearance kick-started a wave of chemical innovation.

All plastics have the same basic structure. Zoom in and most look like strings of pearls, with long, repeating chains that melt when they heat up and set hard as they cool. What makes them special is their versatility. We can extrude them into thin sheets, press them between rollers, blow them into bubbles, cast them like metal or vacuum mould them into 3D shapes. Changing the chemical building blocks of the chains can alter their flexibility, melting point and ability to resist chemicals. Additives between the chains can change their colour, make them fire-proof or kill bacteria, and adding branches to the chains can make them tangle, forming knots that don't melt and locking finished plastics into permanent shapes.

These incredible materials are cheap, clean and waterproof. They can be thick or thin, bendy or brittle, brightly coloured or completely clear. We can wear them against our skin, wrap them around our food and use them to construct everything from pens and tinsel to smartphones and spaceships. Plastics are strong enough to support buildings, light enough to fly and slippery enough to stop eggs sticking to frying pans. But these wonder materials are so cheap that we don't think twice about throwing them away.

Today, we make 300 million tons of plastic a year, half of which goes straight in the bin. We waste 1 million plastic bottles a minute, half a million plastic straws a day and 4 trillion plastic bags every year. Of all the plastic we have ever made, nearly 80% is in landfill or littering the natural world. Nearly a third of plastic packaging goes straight out to sea, where it will stay for several human lifetimes; enzymes made by living things can't touch the human-made chains that make plastic so strong and durable.

+ WHAT CAN WE DO?

The Ocean Cleanup project sits at the very end of the plastic economy, mopping up the river of waste pouring out of our homes and businesses. But, as System 001 scours the sea, people across the globe are stepping up to battle the plastic production line.

The biggest plastic-producing sector is packaging. There are bags, trays and films made from low-density polyethylene (LDPE); milk and shampoo bottles made from high-density polyethylene (HDPE); water bottles and cleaning fluid bottles made from polyethylene terephthalate (PET); plates, cups and cutlery made from polystyrene; insulated packaging made from expanded polystyrene; and bottle caps, crisp packets and ice cream tubs made from polypropylene. Across the world, we use an estimated 10 million plastic bags every single minute. To stem the plastic tide, it makes sense to start here.

Since it launched in 2017, more than 50 countries have signed up to the UN Environment Clean Seas campaign. Single-use plastic is now firmly in the firing line, and countries across the world are phasing them out. Taiwan is ramping up to a total ban on single-use straws, cups and plastic bags by 2030, Zimbabwe plans to ban expanded plastic food packaging, and Kenya has already made plastic bags illegal; people found making, selling or using them face a fine of up to £30,000 or up to four years in prison. They may seem drastic, but these tactics are actually working. In the UK, a 5p tax on single-use plastic bags has seen the number of bags used in England drop by more than 80%.

Bags, straws and microbeads are some of the easiest targets; switching to non-plastic alternatives is cheap and simple. But when it comes to other single-use products like bottles, cutlery and coffee cups, the challenge is greater. One option is to replace plastics with traditional materials. We could use glass, metal, paper, card or jute (vegetable

A LIFETIME OF PLASTIC
We produce it by the ton but use it for a relatively short time

TOTAL
In 2015 we produced a whopping 448 million tons of plastic globally

400

Other (includes health care and agriculture)
52 million tons produced in 2015
5 yrs

2008 RECESSION

Building and construction
72 million
35 yrs

300

Industrial machinery
3 million
20 yrs

Transportation
30 million
13 yrs

200

Electrical
19 million
8 yrs

LEGACY OF WWII
Shortages of natural material led to a hunt for alternatives. This caused a huge boom in plastic production

Textiles
65 million
5 yrs

Consumer products
46 million
3 yrs

100

Packaging
161 million
<6 mth

1973 OIL CRISIS

AVERAGE DURATION OF USE BEFORE DISCARDING

1950   1960   1970   1980   1990   2000   2010   2015

WHY WON'T PLASTIC BIODEGRADE?

Microbes quickly get to work on organic waste, like paper and vegetable peelings, but they can't get to grips with plastic. This might seem odd, as we make plastic from oil, which comes from the remains of ancient plants and animals, but it's all down to the way plastic is made. Natural polymers use chemical links called peptide bonds, while plastic polymers contain carbon-carbon bonds. These bonds are much stronger, and that's both a gift and a curse. Most of the enzymes living things use to break organic molecules down can't manage to break these links. This helps to make plastics so durable, but it also makes them hard to get rid of. There are only a handful of organisms, including some fungi and bacteria, that are capable of breaking them down. Scientists are still working out how best to use them. Ironically, if more organisms learn this trick, it could put the durability of vital plastic structures under threat.

fibre). Yet, while recyclable, these materials aren't always better for the environment. Making paper produces more pollution than making plastic, and it also consumes more energy and more water. And, while glass production is more environmentally friendly, the containers themselves are heavy and bulky, racking up more pollution when products are eventually shipped out.

Creative start-ups are already experimenting with new options, including cutlery made from wheat, water bottles made from seaweed and six-pack rings made from barley. Designed to disappear after you use them, they satisfy the craving for single-use solutions without polluting the planet. But knocking plastic off the top spot will take time. Until then, we need to work with what we've got.

In Japan, there are no plastic bans yet. Instead, they focus on waste management, prioritising recycling so that trash never reaches the sea. Non-recyclable plastics pass through incinerators, releasing heat that turns turbines to make electricity. This approach tries to turn our linear model of product design, consumption and waste into a more circular system. The dream would be to close the loop so that all discarded plastics become raw materials for future production. Changes to design and recycling could make products last longer, make them easier to repair and easier to repurpose at the end of their life, and changes to energy recovery methods could help us to get more out of plastics too contaminated for reuse.

This process is already underway. In Europe, a goal set in December 2017 aims to see 55% of plastic packaging recycled by 2030. But there's only so much we can do in our own homes to recycle the goods we buy. To help us to achieve this goal, policy changes could start to make companies responsible for what happens to their products after we've used them. In South Africa, for example, members of the PET Recycling Company pay a levy on the raw materials for plastic production. This money then goes back into redesigning packaging and recycling post-consumer waste. Not only does this help the planet, it also creates jobs, which can be better for economies than banning plastics all together. Back in the UK, the UK Plastics Pact is working with the packaging sector to transition to reusable, recyclable or compostable plastics. They also want to bring plastic recycling to 70% by 2025.

+SCIENTIFIC INNOVATION

Scientists are experimenting with biodegradable plastics, like polylactide (PLA). This is made from lactic acid, which comes from corn, and it takes just 12 months to break down. For plastics that we can't recycle, new methods hope to capture more energy from waste by turning them into fuels. A process called gasification heats plastics with air to make a gas that can be burnt. Another, called pyrolysis, heats them without air to make a liquid fuel like oil.

There are still problems to iron out with these new technologies. Burning plastic waste can be hazardous, and to make enough biodegradable plastics to replace the real thing we would need to turn over vast areas of land to corn monocultures. Then there is the fact that even though biodegradable plastics can break down, it doesn't mean that they will. They need to reach temperatures over 50ºC, which is achievable inside industrial composters, but not when plastics escape into the ocean. But we're moving in the right direction, and we all have a part to play.

We as individuals can choose alternatives to plastics and put pressure on governments and brands to make bigger changes. If we focus on reduction, reuse and recycling, we could close the loop in the plastic economy and stop this incredible material leaking out into the sea.

MAKE YOUR BATHROOM MORE ECO-FRIENDLY

It's hard to know where to start when it comes to embracing a more eco lifestyle, but the good news is that the bathroom is one of the easiest places to begin

O ur bathrooms rack up a lot of waste – and no, we're not just talking about the natural kind! Think about how quickly our bathroom bins fill up with rubbish. In the average household bin you are likely to find many repeat offenders, from cotton buds to contact lenses and baby wipes. We are living in a world where most products are one-time use and we accumulate a lot of plastic waste because of this, which is having a devastating effect on many of our seaside towns and waterways. It can be overwhelming figuring out where to start, but the bathroom is a great place to begin reducing your plastic footprint. However, it isn't just plastic that is a problem in our bathrooms — there are many other products that also have a detrimental effect on our planet.

+ SUSTAINABLE BRUSHING

Did you know that plastic toothbrushes can take more than 400 years to decompose? One of the easiest and simplest steps to make your hygiene routine more eco-friendly is by switching from a plastic brush to a bamboo one. There are so many companies that offer bamboo toothbrushes now, from those with bamboo handles but non-compostable heads that must be cut off, to fully biodegradable brushes. While many of these eco options are yet to hit mainstream supermarket shelves, you can easily find environmentally friendly toothbrushes online or at most health and eco shops on the high street.

+ SWITCH THE SHAMPOO

Everyday shampoo is not only encased with plastic, but it is also riddled with nasty chemicals like sodium laureth sulfate (SLS), a common chemical found in many shop-bought shampoos. SLS is popular among many brands as it works as the foaming agent to make your hair super-soapy, but many of the sulfates are derived from palm oil. Palm oil is incredibly bad for the environment due to the way that it is extracted and the amount of deforestation that occurs in growing the palm. Shampoo also involves using a one-time-use plastic bottle. However, all of this can be avoided by simply switching to shampoo bars, which can be bought as plastic-free products and avoid some of the harmful sulfates.

+ DITCH THE WIPES

We have a huge addiction to wipes – in fact, we pretty much have a wipe for everything. Yes, they are super-handy with their versatility and durability, from cleaning dirty babies to removing our make-up, but they are alarmingly taxing on the environment and most importantly on our waterways. Many people incorrectly dispose of them by flushing them down the toilet, which in turn blocks pipes and causes thousands of 'fatbergs' worldwide. Fatbergs are a congealed mass in a sewer system formed by the combination of non-biodegradable solid matter. So, what's the answer? Ditch the wipes and opt for another, more sustainable option when it comes to taking off your make-up. One great alternative is a muslin cloth and a gentle make-up remover, or make your own washable wipes from cut-up squares of an old towel.

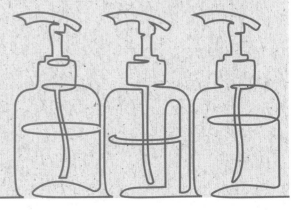

+ TIME YOUR SHOWERS

Get yourself an egg timer and set yourself a limit for the amount of time you are spending in your shower every day. Not only will cutting the shower short save you money on your water bill each month, but it will also make a difference to the environment as you will be reducing the amount of energy required to heat the water. This simple switch can really help to make your bathroom habits more sustainable, as an average shower uses about five gallons of water per minute, so shortening your shower by two minutes can cut your water usage by ten gallons.

+ TURN OFF YOUR TAP

Not only can you switch up your routine by opting for showers over baths to reduce the amount of water you are using, but you can also turn off your taps more elsewhere. Next time you go to wash your hands or brush your teeth, turn the tap off while lathering or brushing.

DRY YOUR TOWELS NATURALLY

Better for your towels and better for the planet

Did you know that tumble dryers are one of the most energy-draining appliances in the home? Obviously they are incredibly handy and avoid any washing lurking around on a clothes horse, but it is far more eco-friendly to allow towels to dry naturally. Allowing them to dry naturally also increases the lifespan of your towels, as they take less wear and tear than they would if they went in a dryer.

SOMETHING OLD, SOMETHING NEW

Go beyond 'shabby chic' and see why there has never been a better time to start upcycling

I t's no secret we're in a climate emergency. The way that we consume things like fashion, food and homewares is unsustainable. According to research by the Reuse Network (reuse-network.org.uk), ten million household items are sent to landfill every single year. But what if we were to do things a little differently and learn to love our things for longer?

Upcycling is not a new concept in itself. Taking something that has seen better days and giving it a new lease of life has long been used by people as a creative way of making do or making something completely unique. For Elizabeth Morris (**@ElizabethDotDesign** on Instagram), it was something she was aware of from a young age:

"Throughout my childhood, my mum was often updating items around the house, repurposing furniture we already owned. I loved getting involved, choosing items from auctions to paint for my bedroom. It's something I've always enjoyed, so when it came to furnishing my own home, I naturally went looking for items to upcycle." This approach went on to have unexpected benefits, as she explains: "I realised that so many people want to fill their homes with unique furniture, but don't have the time or tools to do so – that's where my business began." She launched Elizabeth Dot Design and sells beautiful upcycled furniture through her Etsy store (**etsy.com/shop/ elizabethdotdesign)**.

+ FIX UP, LOOK SHARP

"What I love most about upcycling is seeing a tired piece of furniture transformed to fit within a modern home," says Elizabeth. "I specialise in mid-century pieces, which often look amazing without any paintwork, so I prefer to seek out the pieces that are damaged, stained or broken. I really enjoy the process of fixing these well-built, solid items that have years of use left in them. The paint finish is the final step – I often use bold, graphic designs to hide any imperfections I've fixed, and ensure any salvageable wood grain is highlighted."

Former PR manager Stacy, aka **@TillyAndSage** on Instagram (**tillyandsage.co.uk**), also started out upcycling as a hobby, making presents for people, before it evolved into a full-time business. "I've always had a creative streak

and enjoyed making things... I'd been painting wooden gifts for friends and family when I saw an empty milk bottle in the kitchen at work and I thought I'd try painting that."

The results were really positive, as she explains: "When I posted a picture of it on Facebook I was inundated with requests to make more. That was just over four years ago, and I've run Tilly and Sage full time ever since." For Stacy, it's the creative challenge and satisfaction of the end result that is so appealing: "I just love turning someone's 'rubbish' into quirky items for the home and saving another item from getting sent to landfill."

So far she's rescued everything from jars to old gin bottles: "I've recently started making soap dispensers out of [them]. All my friends and family save them for me... some of the bottles are gorgeous, far too nice to throw away. Instead I upcycle them so that people can get enjoyment for years to come." But her most popular item so far is the festive 'cars in jars'. "These came about because I had some old Matchbox cars that I didn't want to part with. I transformed them into Christmas ornaments and they're a big hit every year. I love scouring vintage fairs and car boot sales looking for the cars!"

✦ LOOK TO THE PAST

Vintage items are also used as a starting point for Suzanne Whitelock's stationery projects. Her business, Pulp Paper Heaven (**@pulp_paper_heaven** on Instagram, or online at **etsy.com/shop/PulpPaperHeaven**), specialises in beautiful handmade notebooks, each one made by reusing original prints saved from the pulping machine.

"I've [always been] drawn to past times," she tells us. "Glamorous movie stars from the '30s, the shapes of fashions from the '20s to the '50s, furniture, household items, sewing patterns, and books and magazines."

As a child, Suzanne used her pocket money to buy treasures from markets, jumble sales and charity shops: "I love the colour and illustration quality of a lot of vintage print. An old book can have a magical air when you think of the many hands that made it and have read it! They inspire me beyond what is written."

Much like Elizabeth, Suzanne also prefers working with

damaged items. "The books and prints I use for binding are worn, torn and crumbly – or, as I like to think, 'overloved'. I can't help imagining all the previous owners, especially when I find interesting inscriptions, recipes, photos or postcards tucked inside." Treasures like this also make their way into her designs: "These get bound back in as part of the new notebook. It's important to keep these snippets of time and people's lives as integral to the book. We all follow our own path, but we criss-cross each other as we go."

+ HOW TO GET STARTED

Feeling inspired and thinking of tackling a new upcycling project, but not sure where to start?

"My main tip would be to be brave and give it a go," says Stacy. "The best thing about upcycling is that your initial costs are very low, so you can experiment with different ideas without worrying about things going wrong and losing too much money."

Whether it's reimagining a new use for an existing item – refashioning old fabric into cushions or clothes for example – anything is possible. Having the freedom to experiment is key. If you're keen on sewing, curtains or bedsheets could become pyjama bottoms, dresses or even a den for little ones.

Happy accidents can produce the most fun projects too. That wool scarf or jumper you shrunk in the wash by mistake? Turn it into a cushion cover! Simply sew the front and back together with a corresponding yarn colour and fill it with a cushion inner. With straightforward projects like these, you'll slowly but surely gather enough unique creations to make your home your own and learn as you go.

What's more, by upcycling furniture, you essentially give a whole room a completely new look for the price of some basic supplies, tools, paint and a bit of spare time. Spending a good chunk of that on prep work will give you a lasting finish, as Elizabeth tells us: "I'm guilty of wanting to see instant results, but I've learnt that preparation is vital if you want the paintwork to last. Give yourself enough time to thoroughly sand, clean and prime before painting. It might be tempting to go straight for the paint tin, but if you don't prep then the paintwork will quickly get chipped and damaged."

BEYOND UPCYCLING
Ways you can make a difference

REUSE
Donating unwanted furniture and electronics to worthy causes such as Reuse Network helps to reduce poverty, cut waste and tackle social exclusion. This organisation alone has helped more than 1.55 million families, saving a whopping 129,250 tons of CO2. Use its fun online calculator to work out how much your unwanted items could help people and the environment. **reuse-network.org.uk**

REPAIR
'Move slow and fix things' says The Restart Project. This organisation helps people learn how to repair broken electronics, as well as rethink how they consume them in the first place. **therestartproject.org**

RECYCLE
Is your item beyond repair? Sites such as RecycleNow or, for those in the US, the United States Environmental Protection Agency (EPA), provide some great tips and advice on how to recycle items safely, helping the environment. **recyclenow. com /epa.gov/recycle**

If you have no room for more furniture, "work with items you love or have some meaning for you," says Suzanne. "It will show in the end result. Practise technique and keep developing new ideas, and you will come up with your personal way of creating that is unique to you."

Outside of this, there are plenty of blogs, Pinterest boards, and relevant hashtags and challenges on Instagram to give you some ideas and motivation to get started. You could even use social media as a way of documenting the process to inspire someone else!

Images Getty Images (bag), Unsplash (crates)

THE PROBLEM WITH FAST FASHION

Unravelling the devastating truth of our love affair with fast fashion

e are addicted to clothes. We're not just talking about our love of shopping – we are also addicted to making clothes. The sad evidence of this is that many fashion companies who used to only offer two collections a year have increased this to anywhere from five to 24 collections. Not only is this incredibly taxing on our increasingly fragile environment, with the fast fashion industry being responsible for producing more than 20% of global wastewater, but it also takes its toll on many of the factory workers, as well as contributing to the ever-growing plastic problem. With its jazzy shop fronts, online deals and deceptively low prices, the fast fashion industry is a consumer's dream, but it's taking a huge toll on our planet – and it's about time we actually did something about it.

+ SEVEN TIMES

According to a a 2015 survey, that's the number of times an item of clothing is worn before it is binned. With the meteoric rise of online shopping and the near-constant stream of new online retailers popping up, it's a tragic but unsurprising statistic. With the rise of social media, many of us are also afraid of being photographed in the same outfit twice, and this is where some of the biggest problems lie. When most people are finished with clothing they donate it to charity shops in the hopes of alleviating some of the guilt of one-wear fashion. However, it's astonishing to learn that when an item is left at a charity shop, it also has a short shelf life of only five to six weeks. If an item is left unsold, it can end up in landfill alongside other household waste. In fact, a staggering 73% of those clothes received by charities and textile sorters worldwide are sent to landfill or incinerated – equating to £82 million in the UK alone..

+ THE SYNTHETIC SNAKE

Do you check your labels before you buy a new item of clothing? If you do, you'll know that many clothes are made from a mixture of polyester, cotton and nylon. So, what's the problem with this? Polyester is a plastic – that's right, you're wearing plastic. We are all aware of the current plastic problem that our oceans are facing, but you may not realise that fast fashion is contributing to this problem. In fact, a wash load of polyester clothes releases around half a million microplastic fibres into our waterways. Sadly, up to a million tons of these are released into our seas each year, damaging ecosystems. The proportion of these synthetic fibres in our clothes has more than doubled since 2000. These fibres are made from oil, which is not only bad for the environment, but also bad for your skin as you're basically wearing petrol. Acrylic clothes are even worse, releasing around 700,000 particles per wash load.

THE INSIDE TRUTH

We spoke to Molly Board, who works for Jacobs Well in India, about challenging the complexities of the fast fashion industry

Q. **Tell us a bit about yourself. Where are you currently working and what's 'Jacobs Well'?**

A. I am a BA graduate of Fashion Design and Technology specialising in zero-waste pattern cutting and sustainability, currently living in Bangalore, India. I am working for a Fairtrade ethical production house called Jacobs Well and I blooming love it!

Jacobs Well is different to your usual factory. For the last 20 years they have been offering education for young girls who've come from some of the poorest slums, orphanages and communities of India. Jacobs Well gives these women hope, a chance at a new life, independence and – most importantly – dignity. Here, these women learn everything from English to tailoring, and they receive support from a regular income. Whether you are an international company or an emerging independent designer, they can oversee a design from conception through to production.

+ A RAINBOW OF DESTRUCTION

A clothing rail full of distinctive colours and prints is all part of the appeal when it comes to shopping, but many of these features are actually achieved using toxic chemicals. After agriculture, textile dyeing is the second-largest polluter of clean water. When these chemicals end up in the water system, many of the people and wildlife in the surrounding areas end up drinking water that can be carcinogenic and detrimental to health.

Q. **Are most fast fashion factories in Bangalore like this?**

A. Sadly not, this is what makes Jacobs Well different to the usual production line. In other factories no fair wage is paid, and often there are not enough man hours to meet the production demand. There are also no health and safety regulations in place, meaning that these women are working in dangerous conditions.

Q. **Can you keep 'on trend' and enjoy fashion but still be mindful of your consumption?**

A. Yes, absolutely! The best thing about recycling and reusing your old clothes is that you can be creative. Instead of reaching for new items, why not try to wear your clothes in a different way? If you are looking for ways to use your summer clothes, then try wearing long-sleeved tops under your summer dresses. This way you avoid having to invest in new clothes every change of season. Another thing to consider is having a capsule wardrobe with neutral colours. Investing and preserving clothes like this provides you with looks that will last you a lifetime and I can guarantee you'll always be on trend.

Q. What five pieces of advice can you give someone looking to minimise their impact on the environment through fashion?

1. STOP CONSUMING

Consumerism is an evil cycle, so it's important that you slow down your purchasing habits. You'll quickly realise you don't need any more. If you do find yourself shopping, then make sure it's necessary.

2. SAVE

Stopping buying allows you to save so much money. Instead of splurging £20 a pop on cheap tops, you can save it and invest it later into something more important.

3. SHOP CHARITY

On the occasion you have the urge to shop, immerse yourself in your local charity shops instead of the high street. Charity shops often have hidden gems lurking on their shelves just waiting to be found.

4. CLOTHES SWAP

A great way of avoiding clothes waste is by swapping your clothes with your friends. Be generous — if you hardly wear something and they really love it, just give it to them. You never know, they might even have an item that takes your fancy too.

5. SHOP INDEPENDENT

Look for independent brands who can tell you the name of their suppliers, where their fabric was woven, and who sewed their garments. Do your research and shop around — these brands do exist!

To learn more about Jacobs Well, check them out on Instagram at **@jacobswellindia**.

THIRSTY WORK

Think you're being kinder to the planet and your wash load with your 100% cotton t-shirt? Think again. While avoiding synthetics like polyester will avoid microplastics (plastic particles of less than 1mm in diameter) finding their way into our oceans, there is still a price to pay for natural fabrics. The average amount of water used for a kilo of cotton, which in layman's terms can be a pair of jeans, is a staggering 10,000 to 20,000 litres.

CARBON FOOTPRINT

Global emissions from textile production equate to 1.2 billion tons of CO_2 – a figure that is so high it actually outweighs the international carbon footprint from flights and shipping combined. Worryingly, a Pulse report predicts these fashion emissions will grow by a whopping 63% by 2030.

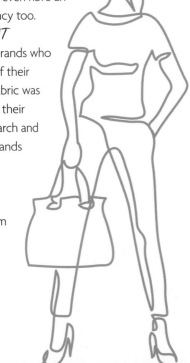

CREATE AN ECO-FRIENDLY WARDROBE

How changing our approach to clothing and shopping can help people and the planet

---

Clothing is the ultimate tool for creative expression. What we wear says a lot about us. But, over recent years, the way we shop for clothes has changed. Gone are the days of having two seasons a year: spring/summer and autumn/winter. If we were to head into our favourite high-street store, we're likely to see new garments and collections every week. To make matters worse, research from Greenpeace shows that around 40% of clothes we own are rarely or never worn.

As most of us already know, this unsustainable quench for something new is affecting our planet. According to **fashionrevolution.org**, global textile production emits 1.2 billion tons of greenhouse gases annually. That's more than that of international flights and maritime shipping combined. Something has to be done. And the best thing? Change really can start in our own homes.

"Every time we buy, wear and dispose of clothes, we create an environmental footprint and an impact on the people who make them, most of whom are women. That's why positive change is more urgent than ever if we are to tackle change and create a more equitable future for all," says Carry Somers, Fashion Revolution co-founder and global operations director.

+ WHERE TO START

First up, let's look in our own wardrobes. Doing an audit of existing clothing – literally laying it all out there – enables us to see what we are really dealing with. Separate the items into piles: to keep, to mend, to donate and to recycle. Be honest with yourself about things that don't suit you, or make you feel less than gorgeous while wearing them. Clothes should be comfortable and enjoyable to wear. This isn't about shaming or punishing yourself either. Have some fun while you're doing it: put some tunes on, get a nice cuppa and have some snacks to give you the fuel to keep you motivated.

Now you know what you've got to work with, you can move forward. What gaps have you noticed? Perhaps your most worn items are a little 'overloved'. Jot down a list of essentials you need for future reference and put it to one side.

+ FIXIN' TIME

When it comes to clothing, wear and tear is inevitable. Bobbles, missing buttons, teeny tiny holes... these are all the signs of a well-loved garment. They're relatively easy fixes too. Try running a pilling comb over your favourite jumper to remove the bobbles. Meanwhile, missing buttons and tiny holes can be sorted in a flash with just a needle and thread required.

Another great approach for bigger holes or stains could be to try a little 'visible mending' – make a feature of its imperfections and let your fixing be on display.

FOLLOW #WHOMADEMYCLOTHES ON SOCIALMEDIA, AS PART OF FASHION REVOLUTION'S ONGOING CAMPAIGN. FASHION REVOLUTION AIMS TO SHINE A LIGHT ON UNETHICAL WORKING PRACTICES AND ENVIRONMENTAL ISSUES CAUSED BY THE FASHION INDUSTRY.

Check out **@TomOfHolland**, **@KatrinaRodabaugh** or the many other beautiful examples on Instagram, using **#visiblemending** for inspiration. Perhaps a pair of trousers or jeans are a little too long, or you'd prefer a different style of cut – from wide leg to regular for example – or maybe a zip is broken. If you're crafty, you might be able to tackle this in your spare time; if you're not, consider attending a local sewing class to learn some new skills. It can be a great way of relaxing after a busy day at work, as well as the added bonus of meeting new, like-minded people. Alternatively, take them along to a local seamstress to fix. You're supporting the local economy, as well as keeping clothes out of the bin.

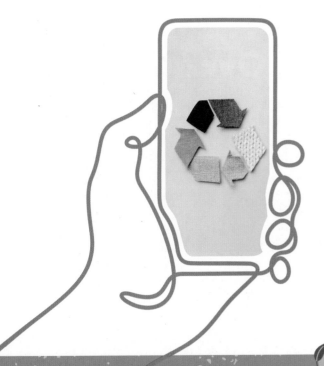

+ RECYCLING AND REFASHIONING

When it comes to your 'recycling' pile, you have a few options. Perhaps you could organise a clothes swap with friends and family? It's a brilliant opportunity to meet up, relax, share a drink and nibbles, and gain some lovely new clothes for your wardrobe.

You could, of course, donate the items to a charity shop; well-worn and damaged clothes could be dropped off at your local textile recycling centre for them to be given a new lease of life. **Loveyourclothes.org.uk** has a list of recycling information on its website.

For those handy with a sewing machine, refashioning is a great way of using up existing resources and transforming them into something you'll actually wear. Great things can be made from the most unlikely of garments. Tents can become dog coats; shrunken jumpers could become cushion covers; curtains or bedsheets could be made into pyjamas, easy-peasy shopping tote bags, play tents or kids' summer dresses. Don't discount fabric scraps either — save them for pincushions, quilts or beeswax wraps.

Better yet, there's a whole community already tackling these sorts of projects, so you'll have plenty of support and help with any questions. A great starting point would be to get involved in the annual Refashioners challenge — head over to Portia Lawrie's blog (**makery.co.uk**) to see what can be done with limited resources and limitless imagination. Pinterest and Instagram also have some great tutorials. When you've finished, don't forget to document and share what you've made on social media or your blog if you have one — it'll help inspire others.

DID YOU KNOW?

Less than 1% of material used to produce clothing is recycled into new clothing.
ELLEN MACARTHUR FOUNDATION

A third of the carbon footprint of clothes comes from the way we care for them.
FASHION REVOLUTION

It takes 2,720 litres of water to make a t-shirt. That's how much we normally drink over a three-year period.
FASHION REVOLUTION

By doubling the useful life of clothing from one year to two years reduces emissions over the year by 24%.
FASHION REVOLUTION AND GREENPEACE

+ BUYING SOMETHING NEW

Switching to more eco-friendly fashion isn't about stopping shopping completely; it's about slowing the process down, doing some research and really considering what we purchase — buying less, but buying better quality. We care about what we eat, and wouldn't dream of buying cosmetics or beauty products that were tested on animals, so it makes sense to take the same approach to clothes. As journalist Lucy Siegle once said: "Fast fashion isn't free. Someone, somewhere is paying."

+ DOING RESEARCH

First of all think about all of your favourite shops and high-street brands — what do you really know about their ethics and working practices? Luckily for us, Fashion Revolution has done some amazing work in this respect. Simply head over to fashionrevolution.org to read this year's report on how each fashion brand fared. The results may surprise you.

Next, it's time to think about fabrics. Opting for an organic fibre is most definitely a good start. "Organic textiles, especially organic cotton, provide solutions to many of the challenges that are related to the increasing consumption of fashion and fabrics," confirms the Soil Association on its website. "Organic cotton helps to combat climate change, use less water, no hazardous synthetic pesticides are used and only low-impact dyes are allowed. It is also better for farmers and factory workers, and GM is banned."

Thankfully, other alternative fabric choices are becoming more mainstream too: bamboo; Lyocell and Modal fabrics (made from wood pulp and beechwood fibres respectively); hemp; and even fruit fibres such as Abaca cotton, made from banana stalks blended with cotton, or Piña silk from the leaves of pineapples.

+ SLOWER SHOPPING

Whatever you're in the market for though, the important thing is to slow down your shopping to really consider what's in your basket. Consider the shapes and styles you feel most comfortable in. So, for example, the list of your 'essentials' that you jotted down can be your starting point, or simply have a look in your laundry bin — what we think is our style and what we actually wear can actually be very different sometimes. According to BBC Earth (**bbcearth.com**), three out of every five t-shirts bought today will end up in the bin within the year — but when we're investing in something we love and brands we support, we're more inclined to wear and repair them.

And, as consumers, the great news is we've never had so much choice. Brands such as People Tree (**peopletree.co.uk**), Thought Clothing (**wearethought. com**), Komodo (**komodo.co.uk**), BAM (**bambooclothing.co.uk**), Veja (**veja-store. com**), Patagonia (**patagonia.com**) and Rapanui (**rapanuiclothing.com**) sell some beautiful, ethically made clothes and accessories to suit a range of budgets.

More and more regular high-street stores are offering organic ranges too, but refer to the Fashion Transparency Index (via Fashion Revolution) for a clearer picture on their working practices. WRAP's (Waste and Resources Action Programme) Love Your Clothes campaign website also has some brilliant information on buying and caring for your clothes: visit the website at **loveyourclothes.org.uk**.

+ INDEPENDENT DESIGNER MAKERS

For those who would like to support smaller brands and businesses, Instagram is a great starting point to seek out like-minded, ethical makers. Check out Nido (**nido-web. com.ar**) who specialises in natural fibres, hand-knitted and hand-dyed with natural products. Not Perfect Linen (**etsy. com/shop/notPERFECTLINEN**) is a family-run brand making stunning clothes from OEKO-TEX certified linen fabric. Green Shoes (**greenshoes.co.uk**) are beautiful, ethical and handmade shoes created by a team in a Devon studio. Whether you choose leather or vegan materials, they're all repairable, which cuts down on waste. Birdsong (**birdsong.london**) states: "We connect women, from worker to wearer," promising products from no sweatshops and using no Photoshop. Birdsong works solely with women's groups and charities to produce its clothing, and everyone is paid above the London Living Wage, so as well as doing your part for the environment, you also know you're doing a good deed for women in need.

+ DIY CLOTHING

If you'd like to take matters into your own hands, creating clothing yourself offers multiple benefits: you know exactly how something's made, you can select environmentally friendly materials, and it's a mindful process to enjoy. Merchant and Mills (**merchantandmills. com**) sells a variety of Tencel (the brand name for Lyocell and Modal) fabrics, while Offset Warehouse (**offsetwarehouse.com**) stocks organic cotton, Modal silk jersey, Ramie and Abaca (pineapple-leaf fabric) at one-metre minimums. When it comes to patterns, shops like Ray Stitch (**raystitch.co.uk**) and Drapers Daughter (**drapersdaughter.com**) stock a wealth of fabric options, along with designs from independent pattern companies. Ultimately, though, whatever approach you decide upon — whether you're creating items to treasure and repairing them when needed, or buying better-quality clothes made using ethical and sustainable methods — these actions will help keep garments out of landfill and in our wardrobes for longer.

KEEP PUSHING FOR CHANGE

+ READ

MENDING MATTERS BY KATRINA RODABAUGH

Katrina's latest book offers quick and easy tips to get started on your mending journey. From patches to stealthy repairs, Katrina covers techniques and how-tos, alongside her essays and thoughts on her slow, sustainable approach to fashion. A really enjoyable read.

katrinarodabaugh.com

+ LISTEN

'WARDROBE CRISIS' PODCAST

Clare Press is the show's presenter, author and Vogue Australia's sustainability editor-at-large. As global ambassador for the Ellen MacArthur Foundation's Make Fashion Circular initiative, she's well-placed to discuss everything from fashion waste, clothing ethics and upcycling with her selection of top guests. Don't miss it.

clarepress.com/podcast

+ WATCH

THE TRUE COST

This hard-hitting documentary about clothing and the people who make them is a must-watch. The film shines a light on unethical manufacturing processes and its victims, as well as the environmental damage the Earth is suffering as a result. Difficult but essential viewing.

truecostmovie.com

+ DO

WASH YOUR CLOTHES AT 30°C

It's said to be just as hygienic as 40°C, but it saves electricity and protects colours. Line dry items if possible, as a tumble dryer can damage clothes. If you don't have outside space, consider investing in a heated clothes dryer.

FAMILY LIFE

How to raise a brood of eco warriors with an appreciation for the great outdoors

*I*t's all well and good making positive changes to your own eco footprint, but what about if you're also trying to raise a family, maybe with a tight budget and busy lifestyle? In some areas of parenting it can seem impossible to be eco-friendly, but have hope that there are always options and alternatives out there, usually found by looking outside the major supermarkets and planning ahead. While babies will rely solely on you to make their choices, teenagers can be much more involved with the day-to-day running of the family household. And if you encounter any hormonal angst, don't get preachy, but mention that it's their future and explain why and how they should get passionate about making a difference.

+ BABIES AND NAPPIES

In our time-poor modern world, manufacturers have come up with increasingly easy and disposable products to help us care for children, from baby wipes and nappies to single-use food pouches. It's so easy to depend on disposable nappies, but these are a major contributor to landfill waste. According to an estimate from OVO Energy, babies use "over 4,000 nappies before they're potty-trained, and on average 5,000 nappies in total, adding up to a whopping 400,000 tons of waste every year – or 2-3% of all British household waste."

The good news is reusable nappies have come a long way in recent years, and actually work out to be much better for your bank balance in the long run. If you're worried about whether they'll work for you, some companies such as TotsBots offer trial kits. Reusable nappies can also be snapped up second-hand on selling sites such as eBay and Gumtree (you can sell yours on too, remember), and many councils offer reusable nappy incentives through vouchers and cashback.

If that wasn't reason enough, today's reusable nappies also come in a variety of prints and colours. Just be sure to line-dry them where possible so you're not running a tumble dryer too often.

If you're still swayed by the convenience of traditional plastic disposable nappies but are concerned about the environmental implications, check out the 'halfway' options that are made from biodegradable material, as these will lessen the landfill impact.

+ SCHOOL YEARS

When kids reach school age, there's always a long list of kit they're expected to have, from school bags and stationery to sports items. Choose notepads from sustainable forests,

and fun backpacks made from hemp, bamboo and recycled plastic bottles. Even mainstream manufacturers such as Nike are now paying attention to their green credentials and offering garments made from recycled materials.

Schools can be demanding in their uniform requirements, but once the specifics have been purchased – think tops with logos – you can get creative by choosing other sustainable clothing bits. **Ecooutfitters. co.uk** is an ethical, sustainable school uniform company set up by two mums who are passionate about improving the standards of kids' uniforms. It's easier than ever to find jumpers and shirts that are not only sustainably made, but Fairtrade, too.

When it comes to lunchboxes, why not choose a sturdy box that will (hopefully) see your kids through their school years? Stainless steel, bamboo and recycled plastic are all material options on the table, and they'll keep lunches just as fresh and tasty.

DITCH DISPOSABLE WIPES

Baby wipes are a massive single-use landfiller that every parent struggles with. While they're convenient, they're also hugely throwaway. If you can't do without them, look for those made from plant fibres such as bamboo (CannyMum Bamboo Dry Wipes are highly rated), which will break down much more quickly. Reusable bamboo cloths are an ideal wet wipe substitute for cleaning up mucky faces and spills, or why not make your own washable wet wipes from old, cut-up towels? You'll save a fortune over the years, and won't be putting nasty chemicals near your little one's skin. Visit **thenappylady. co.uk** for some great 'recipes' for wipes solutions.

+ THE TOY TRAP

Even if you don't indulge in plastic toys, well-meaning relatives and friends might like to buy gifts for your children that are less than eco-friendly. Instead of chastising them for choosing plastic toys, send out a gentle reminder before birthdays and special occasions that you're trying to limit the number in your house, and that you'd much prefer to have days out together or even vouchers.

Baby toys and teethers can be a necessity. Look out for natural teethers such as Sophie La Girafe, which is made from natural rubber, sourced carefully from sustainable farms and fully biodegradable. The adorable, award-winning little giraffe has been going strong for almost six decades, with sales of more than 50 million.

+ GO GREEN WITH THE FAMILY

There are plenty of little ways for older children to go green in their own day-to-day activities, especially with guidance from you as a parent. Encourage them to recycle packaging, conserve energy and reuse or donate items that they've grown out of. Older kids can be taught how to replace regular light bulbs with the energy-efficient kind, turn off plugs and lights when they aren't using them, take showers instead of baths and even print on less paper.

NATURE HOLIDAYS

One easy change that involves the whole family focusing on the great outdoors is to organise holidays around camping, walking or other adventurous activities. Even a couple of days at the seaside can offer opportunities for you to talk about the plants and animals you can see and why it's important to protect their habitats. Rockpooling is another fun activity for children to do at the coast. Conservation volunteering holidays can be an enriching and educational experience for the whole family, but are best left until children are older.

+ FEEDING THE FAMILY

Our food choices hugely impact the way we impact the planet, but filling your family with wholesome and delicious meals can be easily done by shopping more locally, seasonally and making smarter food choices. Advice from the food industry can be a bit of a minefield, though. Should you buy organic? Should you ditch meat and dairy? Are delivery services better value for money and better than driving to the shops?

There are no rules here, but very generally speaking, the best option is to eat as much local food as possible, cut down on meat, include more fruits and vegetables that are in season and avoid items wrapped in plastic. Find your nearest farmers' market and get to know your produce. The kids will love going with you, too, and you can make games out of shopping for the most colourful fruit and veg.

+ MAKE FAMILY EXPERIENCES GREEN

Family life doesn't just take place at home, but through fun days out together. One of the best ways to spark an appreciation for the natural world in your children is to get outdoors with them, whether that's in a local patch of greenery or further afield to designated areas of natural beauty – think country parks, farms and historic sites. Many organisations (such as the National Trust) organise free or very low-cost events for families throughout the year, particularly at key times such as autumn, Easter and during school holidays. With all kinds of events on offer, from woodland adventure days to wildlife watching, these educate children on the seasons, while also keeping them entertained with elements of fun, crafting or games.

Another way to engage children with the natural world is to look for forest schools in your local area, which create a real sense of wildness and natural play instincts. Joining youth organisations such as the Scouts or Guides can also have this effect and will encourage your children to appreciate the world around them.

+ KEEPING PETS

For many of us, having pets is an ingrained way of family life. In the UK, 40% of households have a pet, and the most popular animal companion is a dog (one in four households own at least one). While supporting your local high street is important, websites such as Ethical Pets focus on eco pet items and sell everything you need for a happy, healthy furry friend – think bowls, beds and toys made from waste plant material, natural chews and treats and organic foods. If you buy in bulk and buy quality, none of these items should be more expensive in the long run.

+ TEACH RESPECT FOR THE OUTDOORS

Enjoyment of nature can start in your own back garden. You might help kids plant a tree or get them involved with a vegetable patch. They will love waiting and watching for their plants to grow! Other ideas include setting up bird feeders and birdhouses, with the children taking responsibility for restocking them and seeing which birds come into the garden each day.

The best way to get everyone in the household on board with conservation is to make it fun, so challenge your children to come up with new and game-like ways of going green. Once kids start thinking about their individual efforts – and feel as if they can make a difference – they'll be much more likely to keep up the habits throughout their lives and pass them on to friends and future generations.

THE SCHOOL RUN

Although you can find out lots more about eco-friendly ways to travel on page 114, it's worth thinking about how your children travel to school. If you can walk or cycle with them, you'll be encouraging green travel habits from an early age, as well as getting some much-needed fresh air and exercise as the day begins! If driving is the only option, see if you can regularly share the journey with other kids who live nearby – you'll save time, petrol and will get to know other parents, too.

GO ECO FOR TRANSPORT

Ditch the car and embrace alternative ways to get around

Deep down, we all know that we — as a society — rely far too much on cars to get around and make journeys both big and small. Sure, cars can be convenient, don't get cancelled or arrive late, and provide travel freedom to get us where we need to go. We all want to arrive in comfort, on time and without spending a small fortune, but the environmental implications of making so many car journeys are huge, from driving the need for fossil fuels to polluting the air.

Air pollution is a problem for everyone, even outside major cities. But just how bad is the problem? And why should you care? Although the government sets legal limits for air quality, 'toxic air' has been at illegal levels in London and most urban areas in the UK since 2010, and it's thought that people can be affected by poor air quality even if they don't experience noticeable symptoms such as breathing problems. Local authorities are trying to take actions to reduce the impact of vehicle pollution, such as restricting construction machinery and imposing clean air taxes, but there are plenty of ways you can help to solve the problem on a larger scale, simply by rethinking your regular travel habits.

The number of us driving regularly is even higher than you might have first thought. The National Travel Survey (for England) makes for interesting reading, and in the latest 2018 survey, it was found that almost two-thirds of trips were made via car, with 76% of households owning at least one car (41% own one car, 35% own at least two). The second-highest method was actually walking, at 27% of trips, which sounds great, but this only covered 3% of the annual journey distance. Most of our trips were for leisure (26%) followed by shopping (19%), so we can't even blame our commutes for these figures. So what are the alternative travel methods for longer journeys when walking isn't an option? How can we walk more and for longer distances? How can we change our travel habits to make a positive environmental impact?

+ LIFT SHARING

When you're thinking about the most eco-friendly ways to make your journeys, take into account the number of passengers travelling. Look for car sharing websites such as Liftshare (liftshare.com) that will help you find other road users who are making similar journeys on both a regular and one-off basis. Sharing a car is a guaranteed way to cut emissions, and Liftshare has a business branch of the site that's aimed purely at encouraging coworkers to commute together. Travelling to work together can actually be a fun experience, not to mention the savings you can make by sharing the fuel and parking costs associated with driving to work. Liftshare say that members who share their regular commute save up to £1,000 a year, but if you don't believe that, they've got a handy savings calculator for you to work out your own journey costs. See how much you could save!

+ WALKING

Walking inevitably takes longer than driving (traffic jams excluded) so to incorporate it into your journeys you'll need to find good routes and set off earlier. If you walk to commute, use route planners and walking maps from sites such as walkit.com to find the best ways to get around

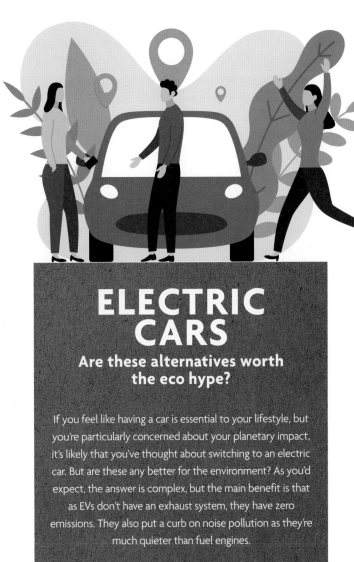

ELECTRIC CARS

Are these alternatives worth the eco hype?

If you feel like having a car is essential to your lifestyle, but you're particularly concerned about your planetary impact, it's likely that you've thought about switching to an electric car. But are these any better for the environment? As you'd expect, the answer is complex, but the main benefit is that as EVs don't have an exhaust system, they have zero emissions. They also put a curb on noise pollution as they're much quieter than fuel engines.

town on foot. To make walking an enjoyable pursuit, get yourself a pair of comfortable trainers and a warm, waterproof coat. If you need extra motivation to move your legs, track how many steps you walk each day – this can be done on most smartphones, with a pedometer or basic activity tracker – and challenge yourself to walk a little further every week! You may have heard it suggested that we should walk 10,000 steps a day (about 5 miles) but new research says the most benefits can be found in individuals who walk on average 15,000 steps per day. Walking has been proven to reduce the risk of many diseases, help to manage weight, and even lower rates of depression. Plus in terms of travel, decreased exposure to busy traffic also reduces stress levels.

+ PUBLIC TRANSPORT

While car sharing (to work or taking children to school) is a better approach than travelling solo, scale that approach up even more and you've got – voila! – public transport! A car might use a quarter of the fuel of a bus, but that car can only carry five people rather than the 60 that a bus might be able to. The obvious public transport methods are the bus and train, unless you live in a city with trams or an underground system. If you're a commuter, look into buying a season ticket, monthly bus pass, railcard or Oystercard for your journeys, all of which offer discounts for regular users. You might even find that your employer offers a season ticket loan, where you pay for travel out of your pay cheque on a monthly basis, instead of one big chunk upfront.

If you're someone who enjoys stats, and want to know just how much you'll be helping the environment by opting for public transport over a car journey, the train company Great Western Railway has a carbon calculator that estimates how your carbon emissions have been reduced when you book a trip.

So to recap, if your destination means you have to drive, carpooling can drastically reduce your CO2 impact on a regular basis, make journeys more sociable and even save you money. But even better, choosing public transportation reduces CO2 emissions by spreading them across many users. For short and easy journeys, though, the ultimate green options are walking and cycling, in order to avoid carbon emissions completely, and they're fantastic for both your mental and physical health.

+ CYCLING

Cycling to work is a great way to keep fit and reduce your carbon footprint, but decent bikes can be expensive. Find out if your employer could help you to pay for a new set of wheels through the Cycle To Work scheme. In the UK this scheme was introduced in 1999, and it still a great way to save money on a new bike, as you won't have to pay the tax. If your employer is part of the scheme (get in touch with your human resources department to find this out) you choose how much to spend on a bike and accessories, then payments come out gradually from your regular pay cheque. You could also look for a second-hand bike on local selling sites such as Gumtree, Freecycle and even eBay. That way, you'll be saving money and also be helping the environment by reusing an unwanted item, rather than getting a new one.

DRIVING ECONOMY

If you have to drive, fine-tune your vehicle

If your lifestyle or location means you have to drive, choose a fuel-efficient vehicle and consider its size. First up, don't get a giant car if you don't need it for regularly transporting goods or lots of people. Inflate your tyres properly, keep your engine tuned, remove excess weight from your car and combine errands to make fewer car journeys. Remember, too, that speeding and unnecessary acceleration can reduce mileage, waste fuel and increase your carbon emissions.

+ TRAVEL SMARTER

According to the National Travel Survey, the two most common purposes for travel (even more than commuting for work) were actually shopping and leisure — think days out, getting to the cinema and sports and hobbies. As these activities are less time-restrictive than getting to work or appointments, they offer the perfect opportunity for you to flex your new eco-friendly travel options at your own pace. Once parking, fuel and car maintenance costs are taken into account, driving not only becomes the most planet-damaging option (and the least fun) but also the most expensive! Next time you go to the cinema, factor in a little more travel time and take a more eco-friendly method.

ESSENTIAL BIKE MAINTENANCE TIPS

Five quick fixes to keep your bike road ready

1 n today's busy world, we've become so accustomed to jumping in our cars to pop to the local shops, or to head to the office, or even to drive to the train station to begin our commutes. It's time to stop relying on four wheels and switch to two! Cycling will not only benefit your health, but the environmental gains are multifaceted. Cycling helps to reduce carbon emissions along with several other air pollutants, noise pollution and traffic congestion that's caused by cars, motorbikes and buses. By choosing to cycle, your individual contribution is greater than you might expect. According to the European Cycling Federation, the average emissions of a car is 313g of CO_2 per kilometre. For cycling, that figure drops drastically to 21g per kilometre – which includes both the initial production and the environmental cost of food (to power the human who's powering the bike!) – a remarkable reduction of more than 93%!

Ensuring you've got the right bike for your needs can make or break your cycling habit; it'll determine whether your bike becomes an integral part of your commute, or languishes in your garage untouched. Consult with your local bike shop to discuss your requirements – not only will they be able to recommend suitable options, they'll help you choose the correct size and provide safety equipment. Most shops offer a free service to ensure your bike remains safe and in perfect working order.

It's vital that you look after your bike to ensure that your rides are safe and enjoyable. As a rule, aim to get your bike serviced every six to 12 months, depending on how often you use it. If you're worried about something on your bike, be sure to get it checked out at your local bike shop. Not everything that goes wrong on a bike needs an expert to fix it, however. From cleaning your bike to replacing an inner tube, we'll walk you through fixing the most common issues you might encounter with your bike.

WHAT YOU'LL NEED

SPARE INNER TUBE | PUMP
2 X TYRE LEVERS
ALLEN KEY SET OR MULTI-TOOL
SOAPY WATER & SPONGE
BIKE CLEANING FLUID & CLOTH
GT85 LUBRICANT

> **TYRE PRESSURE IS A BIG FACTOR IN THE QUALITY OF YOUR BIKE RIDE. IF THE PRESSURE IS TOO LOW, YOU'LL HAVE TO WORK HARDER, AND YOU'LL GET FLATS MORE EASILY. CHECK YOUR PRESSURE AT LEAST EVERY TWO WEEKS.**

MAKE SURE YOU BUY THE CORRECT BIKE PUMP FOR YOUR INNER TUBES. INNER TUBES WILL HAVE ONE OF TWO TYPES OF VALVE – PRESTA (OFTEN ON ROAD BIKES) OR SCHRADER (MOUNTAIN, HYBRID AND KIDS' BIKES).

1 HOW TO CHANGE AN INNER TUBE

1. REMOVE THE WHEEL AND THE TYRE

To remove the wheel, be sure to loosen the rim brake calipers and shift to the smallest sprocket, then use the quick-release skewer to loosen the wheel. For the tyre, insert two tyre levers under the tyre bead approximately 20cm apart.

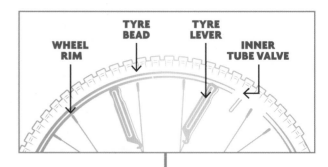

2. REMOVE THE TUBE AND CHECK FOR THORNS

If your inner tube's valve has a locking nut, this will need to be removed. With the tyre still half on the rim, remove the tube and carefully run your fingers along the inside casing of the tyre to find the culprit of your puncture.

3. FIT A NEW TUBE AND REFIT THE TYRE

With the culprit removed, place a new tube into the tyre, and reseat the tyre's bead onto the rim. Be careful not to pinch the new tube in this process. It should be possible without needing the tyre levers. Reinflate the tyre using a pump.

② HOW TO ADJUST YOUR GEARS

1. CHECK THE LIMIT SCREWS

Push the rear derailleur, by hand, as far inward as you can. If you're able to push past alignment with the biggest sprocket, the inward limit screw is set incorrectly. The same applies at the lower end of the cassette. Two small parallel screws will control each limit.

2. BARREL ADJUSTER METHOD

With the bike in a work stand, shift to the problem gear. Then rotate the barrel adjuster situated on the derailleur a quarter-turn at a time. Rotating clockwise will push the chain to a larger sprocket. After each quarter-turn, reattempt the shift until it is crisp.

3. RE-ADJUST THE CABLE

First, shift into the smallest sprocket. Undo the cable pinch bolt, pull the cable taut, then retighten the pinch bolt. Next, shift up and down the cassette to check alignment and use the barrel adjuster to fine-tune.

③ HOW TO ADJUST YOUR BRAKES

1. TEMPORARY - BARREL ADJUSTER METHOD

Most brakes will have a barrel adjuster built into the cable routing. Usually situated at the caliper, a simple twist of this barrel will push the pads closer to the rim to result in a shorter lever travel when braking.

2. RE-ADJUST THE CABLE POSITION

Using one hand, close the caliper so the pads touch the rim. Unscrew the cable pinch bolt, and pull the cable taut before retightening the bolt. Then use the barrel adjuster to fine-tune the pads' position and lever travel.

3. REPLACE WORN PADS

With the bike wheel removed, an Allen key bolt will unscrew the fixings, leaving the pad free to be removed and replaced. Position the pad accordingly so it lines up with the rim, and retighten everything into place.

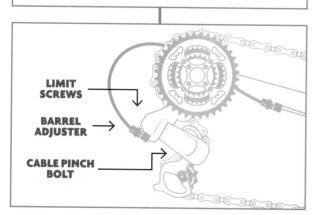

LIMIT SCREWS

BARREL ADJUSTER

CABLE PINCH BOLT

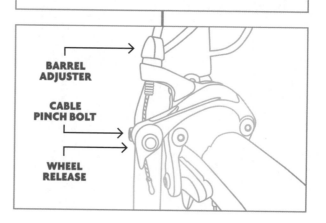

BARREL ADJUSTER

CABLE PINCH BOLT

WHEEL RELEASE

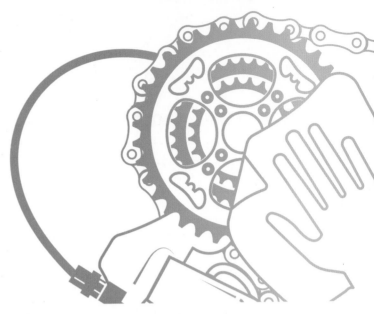

④ CLEAN YOUR BIKE

1. WASH AWAY THE MUD

First up, remove the wheels. With a bucket of soapy water and a large sponge, simply go over the bike and wheels to remove the worst of the grime. Always work from the top down, and ensure the whole bike is drenched.

2. SPRAY THE BIKE WITH CLEANING FLUID

Use a specialist bike-cleaning fluid to coat the bike, leave it for a few minutes, then wipe away with clean water and a clean cloth. At this point, use the cloth to wipe away more stubborn grime and access tight spots.

3. NEVER USE A PRESSURE WASHER

Moving parts are essential to a bike's performance, and grease is used to keep them spinning freely. A pressure washer has the ability to clean this grease out of areas it needs to remain and can ruin a bike, so don't be tempted to use one.

⑤ CLEAN & RE-LUBE YOUR CHAIN

1. CLEAN THE CHAIN

A chain-cleaning tool is optimum, but a clean cloth soaked in GT85 will do. Wrap the cloth around the chain in front of the rear derailleur. Back-pedal the bike so the chain is pulled through the cloth to clean away the grime.

2. CLEAN THE CASSETTE AND CHAINRINGS

Avoid contaminating your disc brake rotor or rim braking surfaces. Use cleaning fluid and a brush to clean the rear cassette and front chainrings. Dedicated tools are available to reach between the cassette sprockets.

3. RE-LUBE THE CHAIN

Back-pedal the bike with one hand whilst lubricating the chain's rollers with the other. Be sure to lubricate the inner surface to ensure the lubricant is spread throughout the drivetrain. Always wipe away any excess lubricant when complete.

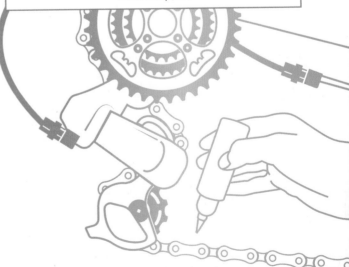

ECO-FRIENDLY TRAVEL

While the rewards of wandering the globe are greater than ever before, so too is the responsibility

A s traditional boundaries to travel continue to disappear, and the world grows increasingly interconnected, more people are exploring the planet than ever before. Despite all of the cultural and financial benefits this brings, travel can have devastating consequences, placing some of the world's most delicate landscapes and cultural gems at risk.

Since international travel exploded in 1950, one million species have become threatened, and vulnerable human populations have been driven to the brink of collapse. Thailand's Maya Bay, virtually unknown a few decades ago, in 2018 became so damaged that the government had to close it indefinitely. In 2016, two-thirds of coral in the

northern Great Barrier Reef was declared dead. Peru, meanwhile, has already had to cap visitor numbers at Machu Picchu, due to the substantial damage caused. One day, it may be closed completely, only viewable from afar.

Travel is a wonderful thing when done right; the greatest mind-expanding experience and ultimate cultural bridge. However, it should serve local communities and ecosystems, not exploit them. Once our natural and cultural treasures are destroyed, it will be too late. The burden to protect them falls on every single traveller, and the time is now.

Sitting at the crossroads of environmental, social and economic issues, eco travel focuses on minimising the impact of tourism. For the uninitiated, it covers all the

variants of ecotourism and green travel, including responsible travel, sustainable tourism and ethical travel. While these terms are interchangeable and vary wildly, their principles remain steadfast: minimise your impact, tread lightly and always leave a place better than you found it. It also promotes environmental and cultural awareness, contributing to conservation efforts and the socio-economic development of local communities.

Fortunately, eco travel's star is on the rise. As the public becomes better educated about the impact of travel on the planet, more people are committing to minimising their own footprints. Whether that's staying at a resort that farms its own food, travelling by land rather than by air, or choosing parks where fees are funnelled directly to conservation, there are myriad options for seeking out greener holidays, ensuring future generations can experience the wonders of travel for years to come.

+ HOW TO PICK A DESTINATION

First, when it comes to choosing a destination, not all are created eco-equal. Some demonstrate a much deeper commitment to Earth-friendly policies, community-centred programmes and sustainable practices than others. Unsurprisingly, Nordic countries lead the pack. Meanwhile, Costa Rica has positioned itself as one of the world's most successful ecotourism destinations. More than 25% of its land – from the beaches of Costa Ballena to rainforests teeming with wildlife – is protected.

Among developing nations, Namibia was the first African country to add the protection of the environment to its constitution, placing conservation at its heart. Meanwhile, 97% of the Galápagos Islands are protected by Ecuador's National Parks Service.

Another emerging eco-Mecca is Uzbekistan. The former Soviet stronghold is now home to a flourishing outdoor culture, with hiking, horseback riding, mountaineering, white-water rafting and bird watching aplenty. It also offers a wealth of alternative accommodation, like eco-friendly yurts, homestays and cooperative-run lodges.

To guide you in selecting the right destination, there are countless rankings listing the world's greenest locales. But, it's just as easy to make an informed decision on your own. Locations with extensive public-transport systems, protected parks, walkable neighbourhoods, and a taste for organic and local produce are usually safe bets. Just avoid the hysterical call to 'go before it's gone'. Travellers flocking to already endangered areas – such as the low-lying Pacific Islands threatened by rising tides; the last remaining Wonder of the Ancient World (the Great Pyramid of Giza); and disappearing Arctic glaciers – only contributes to their destruction.

+ TRAVEL GREEN

The next challenge is how to get there. There simply aren't any green ways of flying, and CO_2 emissions per passenger are astronomical. While the aviation industry is developing bio-fuelled aircrafts, the best option available is to minimise and offset as much as possible. It also helps to book direct flights where possible, to avoid unnecessary fuel-guzzling take-offs and landings.

Another factor towards shrinking your carbon footprint is which class you fly. First and Business produce nine and three times more carbon emissions than Economy respectively. In addition to forgoing the extra elbowroom in favour of conservationist class, carbon-offset programs can go some way to counteracting flight emissions. These schemes enable individuals to donate to green projects – like solar farms, deforestation taskforces and wind-turbine production – to compensate for their own carbon footprints. Renewable projects are considered best, as they directly address the chief cause of climate change: fossil fuels.

While carbon offsetting is not a long-term solution to the problem, it is an effective way of mitigating damage, if combined with other responsible travel practices. But, with hundreds of offset schemes available, it's important to choose the right one. Airlines like Qantas, Japan Airlines, Delta and Cathay Pacific directly offer customers a way to offset carbon emissions.

Elsewhere, look for projects that are certified Gold Standard, Verified Carbon Standard, Voluntary Gold Standard or Certified Emission Reduction, which means they meet the Kyoto Protocol guidelines, an international treaty committed to reducing greenhouse gas emissions. Schemes, such as Terrapass, Carbon Footprint, Cool Effect and Atmosfair, offer a dynamic range of certified projects to offset against.

+ GET AROUND YOUR DESTINATION

How you travel around once you've landed comes with its own moral and environmental quandaries. Cycling, hiking and walking are greenest, but if you need to travel long distances, trains are generally considered environmentally friendly. Buses carrying upward of 40 passengers are the next-best alternative. The most sustainable systems run on electric or alternative power and boast high passenger rates. Switzerland's hydroelectric-powered trains and hybrid buses, along with Japan's lightweight, high-capacity Shinkansen (bullet train), are among the most notable examples.

For seafarers, cruising the open waters can either be a green dream or an environmental disaster. Though sailboats and catamarans are gentle on the planet, cruise ships empty approximately one billion gallons of sewage into the oceans every year, while leaking petrol into fragile ecosystems across the world. In order to help combat the damage, Norwegian cruise line Hurtigruten is exploring greener pastures with the construction of three hybrid ships. These remarkable new ships embrace battery-powered energy, which the company claims cuts CO_2 emissions by more than 20% compared to similar sized cruise ships.

+ WHERE TO STAY

Finding a hotel with an environmental conscience has never been easier, but trusting them with your eco-conscious pennies is more difficult, thanks to less-than-honest proprietors greenwashing their supposed Earth-friendly practices. One way to check out your accommodation's green credentials is through certification programmes. While the Green Hotels Association issues LEED (Leadership in Energy and Environmental Design) certifications to hotels that put environment conservation into practice, Green Key and the Global Sustainable Tourism Council also verify

lodgings truly deserving of their eco-warrior status.

Choosing green accommodation doesn't necessarily mean forgoing a hot shower. Instead, travellers should focus on the issues that matter the most to them, and select accommodation that matches those priorities. While eco-lodges and homestays are often the most sustainable options, many hotel chains and independent properties offer green programmes, such as in-room recycling, composting or only sourcing local produce. Small luxury groups, like Aman, Six Senses and Alila, follow rigorous green practices, while mainstream chains like Accor, Rosewood and IHG have implemented sustainability strategies.

Making environmentally friendly decisions throughout a stay is just as important as choosing the right transport and accommodation. If doing laundry is a must, take clothes to a local facility that supports job creation, and ditch disposable water bottles in favour of BPA-free filtration systems, like Grayl, Lifesaver and LifeStraw.

+ WHAT TO DO

When it comes to sightseeing, there are always plenty of options that are gentle on Mother Nature, like snorkelling, scuba diving, hiking, swimming, kayaking, biking and bird-watching. In addition, visiting craft fairs or markets and purchasing locally produced, artisanal goods supports indigenous communities and farmers – just don't forget to take a reusable bag so that you don't need to buy one while you're out and about. When hunger calls, dine at eco-conscious, fair-labour eateries that serve up locally sourced ingredients.

Finally, when it comes to hiring tour companies, avoid international operators and instead keep your eyes peeled for local, environmentally friendly businesses that employ, and fairly compensate, local guides. Not only are you empowering the native population and helping to generate income, but you'll get a guide with a deep-rooted knowledge and understanding of the destination, and will receive a more authentic experience than you would if you opted for an international guide.

THE JOY OF STAYCATIONS

Planning your next holiday? Sometimes you don't need to look much further than your own back yard

As the dark nights draw in, it's tempting to dream of escaping to warmer climes... but making this dream a reality literally costs the earth. The airline industry dumps more carbon emissions into the air than any other form of transport. But that doesn't mean you have to forgo your holidays – far from it. Your passion for sustainability gives you an amazing chance to explore all the wonderful things your home country has to offer. Go on a 'staycation'! You'll become a local expert, knowing all the best places to go for food, photos and adventure. All while saving the planet. So, hop on a train and head to an exciting domestic destination.

There are so many benefits to a staycation. Forget stressing about baggage allowance, carry-on liquids and getting to faraway airports – say hello to a holiday that's no more than a few hours away and involves minimal preparation. You'll be able to take as much stuff as you can carry, then choose an eco-conscious mode of travel, be that a bus, train, or even a bike. If you've got a pet, you may even be able to bring them along with you!

It's also easier to be greener in your own country than it is abroad, as you know where to buy environmentally friendly food, products and souvenirs. You can shop from ethical companies, and you will instantly know how to recycle things once you've finished with them.

Plus — and this is a big one — a staycation can be much cheaper than a big trip abroad. Think of all the money you'll save on airfares, visas and currency exchanges — use it to treat yourself to something instead.

A staycation can easily give you everything you're looking for in a holiday. How many close-to-home places have you seen, sworn you'd go to one day, and just never found the time? Now's your chance to tick those things off your bucket list. Head to that beautiful historic building, or do that awesome hike you saw on TV. Perhaps you know of a secluded spot the other tourists will find tricky to get to. There will always be places you've never been to, and new experiences to enjoy. The best thing is, they're easy and inexpensive to reach.

Domestic tourism will also allow you to appreciate your home so much more. You'll have the space to truly breathe and relax, and to observe all the good things around you. Imagine taking a walk in a quiet forest, or ziplining through a valley you didn't even know existed. There's so many adventures to be had just outside your back door — sometimes all you need to do is look for them.

SIMPLE STAYCATIONS

✦ ADVENTURE HOLIDAY

Fancy a hike through deep forests, or trying out new watersports? Most countries have gorgeous natural surroundings that offer plenty of opportunities for adrenaline-pumping fun.

✦ BEACH

If you like nothing more than to chill out on the sand, a beach (or even a lake) is never too far away. Don your flip flops and your suncream, and take a trip to the beach with your friends.

✦ CITY BREAK

Your home country is probably full of cool towns and cities you've not visited. Think historic centres, cool music venues and swanky restaurants — they're just waiting for you.

✦ HOME TIME

Sometimes a staycation can be as simple as chilling out at home. You could read that book you've had on your shelf for ages, learn a new skill or just relax in your garden or the park.

PART TWO: TAKE ACTION

—

There's only so much that we, as individuals, can do. The rest is up to politicians to pass laws to fight the climate crisis, or big companies to improve. In this section, find out how you can trigger change from the top, from inciting change in companies on page 120 to writing to local political figures to encourage them to reflect your views on page 116. Taking collective action needn't be on such a grand scale, however. Encouraging family and friends to consider a more eco-friendly lifestyle can be a tough task, but more people than you think might be open to change. On page 106, find out sympathetic ways you can communicate with family and friends about embracing a more sustainable lifestyle. Similarly, on page 108 you might be interested to find out how you can get involved in your community to spread the word.

IT IS THAT EASY BEING GREEN

Want to convince others to be more eco-friendly? Here's how...

With the new year, many of us may look to make an eco-friendly change to our lifestyles. Perhaps that's why you've picked up this book – in which case, go you! If you have been inspired to go green, that's fantastic. Maybe you would like to encourage others to do the same, but aren't quite sure how to go about it. It can be tricky to strike a balance between being keen and being too forceful, but don't worry, this guide is here to help you.

The first step you can take is to share information and resources – particularly the things that inspired you to change. After all, if they were powerful enough to convince you to rethink your habits, chances are they could do the same for others. Whether it's discussing a shocking documentary you saw, or posting a link to a news article with some hard facts, any information can really help your case.

Alongside those, you might also wish to send people some helpful tips on going green right away. Even small changes, such as buying less plastic, can go a long way. If the person you're thinking of is already reconsidering their carbon footprint, they're likely to be very receptive to any advice, and looking for new ways to be more sustainable. You can even show them just how easy it is by giving them some inspiration from your own life – whether you've switched to biodegradable bamboo cotton buds, or you use old plastic pots as handy storage containers, there are a million ways to make a change today.

With that in mind, it's also a good idea to show people how fun sustainability can be, as well as being necessary to the future of our planet. You could get outdoors and help plant trees, giving you and your friends a sense of achievement at the end of the day. Or, you could organise a clothing and accessory swap with them, to get the buzz of wearing new clothes without contributing to unethical garment industry practices. Meet new people by taking friends along to a community beach clean – the opportunities are endless.

One of the main reasons people struggle to change their lifestyle is because they feel they don't have time. But more often than not, that simply isn't true – they can simply replace the things they already do with environmentally friendly alternatives. Single-use plastic is a great example of this. Suggest they stop buying bottles of water when they're out and about. There are so many refillable options on the market now – it takes seconds to refill a bottle, plus it's so much cheaper. The same is true for most other packaging, too. When the topic arises, gently point this out – you might just change their mind.

Another effective strategy is to demonstrate that making sustainable choices doesn't have to be expensive.

In fact, it can often save you money. Switching off things (from the socket) when you aren't using them saves a surprising amount of energy. Installing cavity wall insulation onto your home is relatively inexpensive, and can save you a lot on your heating bill. When it comes to your wardrobe, buy fewer clothes, and recycle your old ones when they become worn, and you'll save a significant amount of cash over the year.

There are so many other things you can do to encourage others to follow your eco-friendly lead – be the example for them to follow. The key thing to remember is to always be positive, encouraging and non-judgemental, and you'll soon become the eco warrior you were born to be.

> GIVE YOUR FRIENDS GREEN GIFTS ON THEIR BIRTHDAYS. TREATING THEM TO SOME LOVELY NATURAL SKIN PRODUCTS OR A FUNKY STAINLESS STEEL WATER BOTTLE COULD JUMPSTART THEIR JOURNEY TO BECOMING GREEN.

CONNECT WITH YOUR COMMUNITY

Take environmental action together with people in your community to expand your impact and boost your own happiness

T he enormity of the climate crisis and other environmental challenges can make tackling them seem quite daunting. It's less overwhelming to focus on a particular environmental issue and engage with your community to tackle it. To decide what to focus on, look at what's relevant to the community and what you are most passionate about. Select an issue that excites and energises you instead of one that fills you with hopelessness or fear. To make a community contribution

to solving the climate change crisis, consider energy, buildings, transport and food, the primary greenhouse gas emission sources. Which of these areas excites you the most? What concrete changes in that area would improve the quality of life in your community? Would you like to see better cycle paths, more energy-efficient housing that lowers energy bills, or people eating a healthier, plant-based diet?

+ BE A HAPPY HERO

Being clear with yourself about what you want to achieve is essential, but it's vital to be equally clear on why you want to take community action. A strong, positive motivation makes you persevere with the work over time — and consistency is key to creating change. Beyond the direct benefits to your own quality of life from, say, reduced air pollution or lower energy bills, making a difference to others also enhances our own well-being. Feeling good by doing good is what sustainability expert Solitaire Townsend calls 'happy heroism'. Doing good together with your community instead of on your own can boost your happiness even further: feeling a sense of belonging with a social group, and having something in common with the others in the group, is linked to high levels of life satisfaction.

+ FIND YOUR PEOPLE

Once you have determined which issues to focus on and clarified your motivation, find other people in your community to join your mission. This can be the people in the geographical area where you live, people you work with, people who share your profession, or people that you share other interests with — you may consider yourself part of a community of artists or runners or parents, for example. Find out whether an environmental or climate change group already exists within this community, and if so, whether that group is already working to address the particular challenge you want to solve. If you can't find a group, start your own. Speak to friends and colleagues, post flyers and use social media. Avoid relying on fear-mongering or the doom-and-gloom narrative so often associated with environmental activism. Instead, share your own positive motivation for acting to make others equally inspired.

+ BUILD SOUND FOUNDATIONS

Creating change is all about relationships," say Friends Of The Earth, the world's largest grassroots environmental

CONNECT
Many environmental organisations have a global network of local groups

- **FRIENDS OF THE EARTH** is the world's largest grassroots environmental network.
- **THE TRANSITION NETWORK** is a global network of community groups that aim to transition to a low-carbon, resilient future by organising projects within the areas of food, transport, education, housing, arts and energy.
- **350** is a global movement of people focused on ending fossil fuel use and replacing it with community-led renewable energy.
- **GREENPEACE** runs local groups that aim to defend the planet.

network. They recommend that the first few meetings of your community group are informal and relaxed. First, get to know the members of the group — who they are, why they are there, and what skills and passions they bring to the table. Second, discuss what you want to do — set out what excites you and what action is needed in the community. Once you all agree on a common mission, set out ground rules for how you will operate. Third, create a strategy for action. Initial actions can include awareness-building activities with the simple aim of growing a following. Think film screenings, blogs or an article in the newspaper. Then, get started on implementing concrete actions to achieve your goal.

+ IMPLEMENT CONCRETE ACTIONS

Community energy is a big area for local action around the world. This includes any collective action to reduce, purchase, manage and generate energy, such as community-owned solar panels or wind turbines. Community-level renewable energy is particularly attractive in communities in developing economies, where traditional energy access is absent or limited, but it's also increasingly popular in developed economies — in the UK alone, at least 5,000 community groups have undertaken energy initiatives in the last five years.

It's not just energy initiatives, though. When it comes to food, examples of community action you can take include urban agriculture initiatives, establishing food belts to enable more local food production, and planting trees that are productive, such as nut and fruit trees.

Or maybe you're passionate about nature-based projects? This is another prime example of how communities can come together to take action. Protection of forests and wildlife, restoring degraded land and mangroves, sustainable fishing... the list of action areas is extensive. The Equator Initiative — equatorinitiative.org — showcases examples of communities pioneering sustainable development and nature-based solutions to climate change. Their database includes more than 700 projects — why not take a look for some inspiration?

5 LESSONS FROM A SUCCESSFUL CLIMATE COMMUNITY CAMPAIGN

A community initiative in the small English town of Ashton Hayes reduced emissions by 24%

1. POSITIVE FOCUS
Rather than guilt-tripping people, campaigners focused on positive motivation. They presented energy- and cost-savings as non-idealistic reasons to act.

2. MEASURE PROGRESS
A university professor volunteered to track carbon emissions in the community over time.

3. WORD OF MOUTH
The campaign relied on neighbours and friends spreading the word.

4. SHARE SUCCESS STORIES
Any original action that saved energy and money was shared across the community.

5. KEEP IT LIGHT
Meetings were informal and welcoming.

+ SHOUT ABOUT IT

Once you've achieved your goal, or started progressing towards it, share your success story to encourage others to act too. You can inspire others in your community to join your efforts by writing a piece for the local paper or sharing your success on social media, but you can also inspire other communities to launch their own initiatives. The rural town of Ashton Hayes (see above) achieved a 24% reduction in greenhouse gas emissions over the course of a decade through community action, and hundreds of other activists, towns and cities around the world have contacted the townsfolk looking for guidance in launching their own community programmes. The more people you influence to act, the greater your impact.

HOW GOVERNMENTS CAN SOLVE THE CRISIS

Governments around the world recognise the need to act on climate change, but action needs to be more ambitious

Solving the climate crisis requires rapid, large-scale system change. Relying solely on changes in individual behaviours, like moving towards a vegan diet or switching to a renewable energy supplier, are a great place for individuals to start, but they won't transition our societies quick enough. When it comes to other huge social or economic challenges, such as education and unemployment, we rely on governments to play a central role in driving solutions. Through policies, incentives and regulations, governments have extensive power to set the direction our societies take. Governments can influence whether we build coal power plants or solar farms, whether we drive cars that run on petrol or electricity, whether our buildings are energy efficient or not... and as a result, whether we solve the climate crisis in time.

IN 2012, A STUDY ASKED MPS OF EIGHT EUROPEAN COUNTRIES FOR THE MOST EFFECTIVE WAYS FOR CITIZENS TO INFLUENCE CHANGE. THE TOP ANSWER? VOTE.

+ A GLOBAL CLIMATE AGREEMENT

Around the world, governments recognise the need to collectively tackle the climate crisis. In 2015, 197 parties signed up to the global Paris Agreement on climate change action, which aims to limit the global temperature rise this century to "well below 2ºC above pre-industrial levels and to pursue efforts to limit the temperature increase even further to 1.5ºC." The Paris Agreement also aims to prepare countries to cope with the impacts of climate change that are inevitable due to the greenhouse gases already released into the atmosphere. Already today, the world is 1ºC hotter than it was in 1880.

The universality of the Paris Agreement was hugely important. Addressing climate change has positive economic benefits in the long-run, but it requires investments up front in renewable energy, low-carbon transport solutions, energy-efficient buildings and sustainable agriculture. A key political challenge around climate change is if one country invests today to radically cut emissions, but the rest continue as usual, the leading country will not experience any less climate change in the future than everyone else. Greenhouse gas emissions, unlike, say, air pollution, are not local. As a result, no government wants to lead alone. With the Paris Agreement, all governments committed together to a low-carbon, climate-resilient future – until in 2017, the United States, after a change in presidential leadership, pulled out. Fortunately, the withdrawal of the world's largest economy has not derailed the Agreement. "Other countries have stayed in and doubled down on their general determination not to walk away, not to let the US 'cancel' the agreement," said former US climate envoy Todd Stern in 2018.

Despite the Paris Agreement remaining intact, country-level pledges to cut emissions are not ambitious enough. Per September 2019, country-level pledges put us on track for temperatures rising up to 2.9ºC. What's more, current policies are also not sufficiently strong enough to meet the pledges. If governments keep with their current policies, we are headed for a temperature rise of 3.2ºC.

+ LEADERS AND LAGGARDS

Collective government climate action is falling short, but some governments are pulling their weight. On top of the leadership board, The Gambia and Morocco are the only two countries with policies aligned with limiting global heating to 1.5ºC. Bhutan, Costa Rica, Ethiopia, India and the Philippines all have policies that are compatible with a 2ºC increase. The downside? This crop of leading climate performers are all minor emitters, with the exception of India.

At the time of writing, the worst performers, whose policies put us on track for more than 4ºC of global heating, are Russia, Saudi Arabia, Turkey, the US and Ukraine. Many of these lagging countries are large and have a significant impact on the global total of emissions: US, Russia and Saudi Arabia are all in the top 10 of largest emitters globally, so it's imperative that these governments pull their weight.

+ THE POWER OF LOCAL

Unleashing the power of national governments is crucial to solve climate change, but local governments – particularly cities – are also important players. When the national government is lagging behind, other levels of government can step in to fill the gap. After the US federal government announced that they would be pulling out of the Paris Agreement, California governor Jerry Brown and former New York mayor Michael Bloomberg led the 'America Pledge' movement, where cities and states – as well as businesses and universities across the country – committed to still contribute to the US achieving its Paris Agreement goals. The US states of California, New York and Hawaii have all set net zero targets. In Australia – another climate laggard at the national level – the states of New South Wales, Victoria, and Queensland are also aiming for net zero.

At the city level, 94 of the world's largest cities, representing as much as a quarter of the global economy, are committed to delivering on the most ambitious goals of the Paris Agreement at the local level through the C40 Cities initiative. What cities do on climate change matters: By 2050, more than two-thirds of the global population is expected to be urban, so finding a more sustainable way to live in the city is a vital step to saving our planet.

+ GLIMMERS OF HOPE

In 2019, several national governments stepped up their game on climate. In June, the UK became the first major

INDIA'S CLIMATE LEADERSHIP
Policy commitments drive a rise of renewable energy

India is now investing more in renewable energy than in fossil fuels. According to the Climate Action Tracker, "interventions in [India's] electricity sector have largely been driven by strong policy commitments." The transport sector is experiencing more policy uncertainty, though. A National Electricity Mission Mobility Plan aims to offer incentives for adopting and manufacturing electric vehicles, but the government has moved away from their initial target of electric vehicles accounting for 100% share of new sales by 2030.

A ROADMAP TO THE UK'S NET ZERO TARGET

A target must be followed by policies

Ambitious policies need to follow the UK's 2050 target that was made into law in June 2019. The Committee on Climate Change recommends that the government ban new petrol and diesel cars from 2030, a decade before the current 2040 target. Other areas where the Committee recommend policy action include tree-planting, low-carbon heating solutions and carbon capture and storage solutions in heavy industry.

economy to pass into law a target of net zero emissions by 2050. Shortly after, France followed suit. A total of 77 countries have now made commitments to reach net-zero emissions by or around 2050, but the solidity of the commitments varies. At the city-level, net zero targets have been made by the likes of New York City, London, Paris, Sydney, Stockholm, Barcelona, Copenhagen, Helsinki, Manchester, Oslo, Reykjavik and more.

Setting net-zero targets and making them law is a valuable step in the right direction. However, targets are only valuable if they are implemented. All high-level commitments need to be followed by detailed roadmaps on how to get there. Immediate policy action is needed, like the announcement from 30 countries, 22 states or regions, and 31 corporations that they will stop building coal-fired power plants in 2020, made in September 2019.

+ DEMAND GOVERNMENT ACTION

Solving the climate crisis requires government leadership across international, national and local levels. Individual action on climate change matters too, but one of the most impactful action individuals can take is to push governments to take radical climate action on their behalf. Now is the time to demand political action. 2020 is the deadline for countries to declare further emission cuts as part of the Paris Agreement process. Signs of progress are emerging, as 67 countries have expressed intentions to enhance their commitments — but most of the largest economies are still falling short. Leading governments, whose plans are already aligned with solving the climate crisis, need to be examples for others to follow.

LOBBY FOR CLIMATE ACTION

Write to your elected representatives to push climate action up the political agenda

---

Government action is essential to solve the climate crisis. Voting is often the primary tool that comes to mind when we think of influencing politicians to act on our behalf, but we can exercise our democratic rights at any time by writing to our elected representatives and demanding action. Politicians want to respond to the concerns of their constituents to increase their chances for re-election. While local representatives may not be able to directly change policies and laws, they will pass their constituents' concerns up the political food chain to ministers and other senior policy makers. "Taking one action at one point in time may seem insignificant," says Amnesty International, "but change comes from sustained pressure over time, from a collective voice – of which you are one."

+ UNDERSTAND THEIR PERSPECTIVE

Before reaching out to your local representative, research their position and political interests. If you can present your concerns in a way that aligns with your representative's own interests, they are more likely to assume an active role in getting your concerns addressed. If you know that your local representative is passionate about reducing air pollution, you could point out that rolling out public transport solutions and electric vehicles to reduce greenhouse gas emissions from transport would simultaneously improve air quality. "If you can approach from an angle they are already sympathetic with, there is a much higher chance of getting your message across," says the Campaign Against Climate Change.

You can typically find information about the position and political interests of your local representatives on government websites. Checking your local representatives' social media accounts can give further clues on their primary and immediate areas of interest.

THE CASE FOR CLIMATE ACTION

Reminding politicians of the positive impacts of climate action can incentivise them to act

Taking climate action will have significant benefits to the global economy, while failing to address the climate crisis comes with huge economic risks. According to the Global Commission on the Economy and Climate:

- Low-carbon economic growth could offer US$26 trillion of direct economic benefits through to 2030 compared to business-as-usual.
- By 2030, climate action could generate more than 65 million new low-carbon jobs.
- Climate action would avoid more than 700,000 premature deaths from air pollution.

+ BE PERSONAL — AND POLITE

Politicians take more notice of personal messages than standardised emails. Take the time to write about your own view instead of copying a template — it signals a stronger level of concern. Demonstrating that climate change is relevant to a large share of local people will strengthen your case, as will including relevant statistics. Your representative will need figures and facts to build a case for action with other politicians. And remember, be polite to be taken seriously!

+ DEMAND SPECIFIC ACTION

Campaign Against Climate Change suggests three key messages to include: First, that climate action is urgent. Second, that current policies are insufficient. Third, that the government needs an action plan that is sufficiently ambitious to align with the Paris Agreement on climate change.

You can then drill down into more detail, such as requesting action on clean energy, smarter urban development, sustainable agriculture and protection of forests, water management and a circular economy, five action areas of the low-carbon transition highlighted by the Global Commission on the Economy and Climate. Depending on where you live, one or two areas of action may be more crucial to single out. Or take a more strategic approach and demand action in areas your local representative is especially interested in or has particular influence over.

End your email or letter by requesting that your representative pass on your concerns to the relevant minister, and ask that they add their own support if they agree with your views.

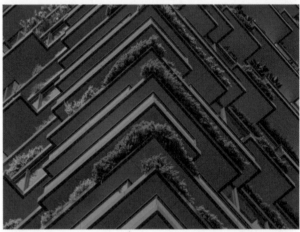

READY, SET, WRITE!

What to say when writing to your local representative

Share why climate change is an important issue to you and why you are writing. For example, briefly refer to a specific piece of recent news that sparked a reaction in you.

—

Ask your local representative to forward your letter to the relevant minister, and ask that they add their own support if they agree with the views and arguments you have put forward.

—

Request that your local representative takes specific action on climate change on your behalf.

Set out the problem clearly. Highlight that climate action is urgent and that current policies are insufficient.

—

Set out specifically what you are asking for: a concrete government action plan that is sufficiently ambitious to align with the global Paris Agreement on climate change. Add any specific areas where you would like to see action.

—

Ask for a response.

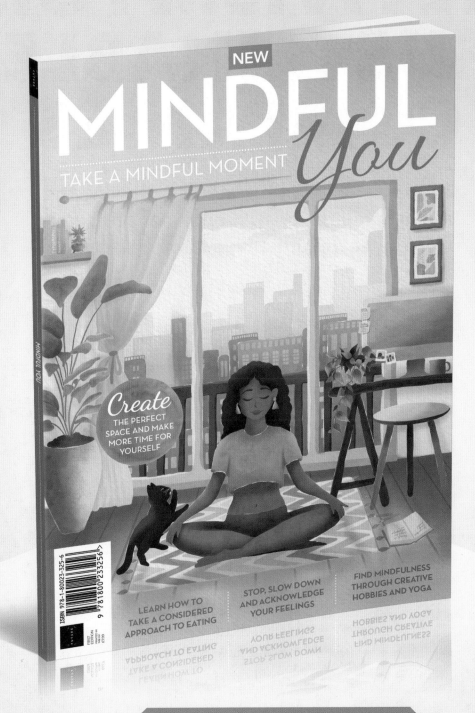

CONSUMER ACTIVISM FOR SUSTAINABLE COMPANIES

Businesses play a central role in solving the environmental crisis. Consumer pressure can incentivise them to ramp up action

E nvironmentalists often position big business as the enemy of environmental sustainability. Businesses contribute to deforestation, the biodiversity emergency and pollution. Just 100 businesses account for 71% of global greenhouse gas emissions. Corporates are hugely powerful: 69 of the top 100 economic entities in the world are companies. While this power can be used for environmental destruction, it can also be applied to advance environmental sustainability. Businesses are key contributors to environmental problems, so are also essential players in solving them. Companies are increasingly recognising this responsibility and ramping up action on environmental sustainability. IKEA, for example, aims to be 'people and planet positive' by 2030. Corporates all need to move much faster, which is where consumer pressure comes in.

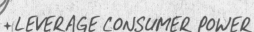

⁺ LEVERAGE CONSUMER POWER

By changing their purchasing behaviours, consumers can pressurise companies to be more environmentally ambitious. Consumer demand is a great motivator to improve corporate environmental performance. In a 2019 survey of European business leaders, 41% said consumers were 'very influential' in driving the environmental performance of their business. However, there's a gap between consumers' intentions and actions, and overcoming this will fully leverage the potential of consumer pressure for sustainability: While 65% of consumers say they want to buy from sustainable brands, only 26% follow through in their purchasing decisions. That said, even consumers' intentions can influence companies to change. When companies design their environmental sustainability strategies, they consider the expected priorities of tomorrow's consumers, as well as the purchasing patterns of today's.

To strengthen the signal to companies that environmental sustainability is an urgent priority, consumers can take a range of actions, which we'll cover over the next few pages.

THERE'S AN APP FOR THAT

The Good On You app provides consumers with sustainability ratings on 2,200 fashion brands

The Good On You app offers a five-category ranking — ranging from 'we avoid' to 'great' — across the areas of people, planet and animals. The app covers both popular high street brands and smaller eco-brands. As a consumer, you can search by brand name or product category. If the brand you look up has a low ethical rating, the app suggests an alternative option that is higher-rated but similar in style and price.

⁺ MAKE NOISE ONLINE

Individual consumers can also raise their concerns over a company's environmental performance on social media, as a complement or alternative to boycotting. The public nature of a social media post means that individual consumers can put much more pressure on companies than they used to be able to, back in the day when individual complaints to a company were contained in letters or phone calls. Companies may care somewhat about losing the custom of one individual, particularly if that person was previously a loyal customer, but they care a lot more about losing the support of hundreds, thousands or even millions of potential consumers from a viral social media comment.

Consumers can also engage with organised social media campaigns spearheaded by environmental organisations. Back in 2010, Greenpeace launched a social media campaign to protest against Nestlé using unsustainable palm oil, a significant driver of deforestation. The Greenpeace campaign centred around an online spoof advertisement for the chocolate bar KitKat, a brand owned by Nestlé. Greenpeace used the video to drum up attention for the issue and called for supporters to criticise Nestlé on social media or email the company's CEO. After 1.5 million views of the fake advert, 300,000 consumers flooded the CEO's inbox with demands for

change. Shortly after the campaign, Nestlé announced that none of their products will be associated with deforestation by 2020.

✦ SUPPORT SUSTAINABLE COMPANIES

Putting negative pressure on companies can be effective to get them to change practices or policies, but it is not the only option for consumers who want to see companies up their game on environmental performance. Actively directing purchasing towards companies that perform well on environmental sustainability, so-called BUYcotting, sends an equally strong signal. While boycotting remains more widespread amongst consumer activists, BUYcotting is on the rise, particularly amongst younger people. Out of 1,000 surveyed consumer activists, 91% had engaged in boycotts, with only 58% engaging in BUYcotting – but 29% expected to step up their BUYcotting in the next two years, compared to 22% expecting to increase their boycotting efforts. From 2013 to 2018, products marketed as sustainable grew 5.6 times faster than other products. Business leaders are taking notice of this trend. For example, food products company Danone aims to make all their brands 'Manifesto Brands' – brands that improve the health of people and protect the planet – as the 40 Manifesto Brands it currently has are growing faster than the company's other brands.

FOLLOW THE LABELS

When shopping, look for labels and certifications to find the most environmentally sustainable product options

Environmental charity WWF suggests consumers select:
- Products with recycled content, such as recycled toilet paper and kitchen towels.
- Sustainably sourced wood. Whether shopping for furniture or notebooks, look for the Forest Stewardship Council (FSC) label.
- Sustainably produced food. Select MSC-certified seafood and organic food. For processed foods, look for certified sustainable palm oil (more generally, plant-based alternatives to meat and dairy have much lower environmental footprints).
- Energy-efficient appliances and equipment.
- Biodegradable cleaning products.

+ NUDGING FOR GOOD

Consumers have extensive power to influence companies to provide environmentally sustainable products and services, but there are still limitations to consumers' ability to act, since purchasing decisions are hugely influenced by corporate marketing and 'choice-editing', such as where a product is positioned in a shop.

Consumers may like to think they are fully rational in their decision-making, but that's not necessarily the case (see 'Nudging For Sustainability', right). Being aware of this subconscious aspect of purchasing decisions allows consumers to demand that companies intentionally use their consumer influence to make it easier for consumers to choose sustainable products – rather than using this impact simply to maximise their own financial profits.

Retail company Tesco, for example, is exploring the idea of nudging their customers towards both healthier and more environmentally sustainable food options, instead of conventional point-of-purchase offerings.

NUDGING FOR SUSTAINABILITY

Companies can use marketing and choice-editing to help consumers buy sustainable products and services

Companies can use insights of human decision-making to influence customer behaviour towards environmentally sustainable options. Even something as simple as telling online shoppers that others were buying environmentally sustainable products led to a whopping 65% increase in shoppers making at least one sustainable purchase. As companies then see a further demand increase for environmental sustainability, they will ramp up their efforts, and a virtuous cycle will be at play.

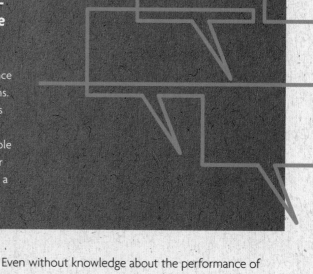

+ KNOWLEDGE IS POWER

Regardless of which avenue of action a consumer wants to take, knowledge about the current environmental performance of a company or brand is a prerequisite to engage. Consumers need to know who to buy more from, who to avoid, who to praise on social media, and who to 'name and shame'.

At the company level, consumers can look to rankings of sustainable businesses to guide them. Consumer giant Unilever, whose products are used by 2 billion people globally every day, came out on top of the 2019 GlobeScan/SustainAbility survey of sustainability leaders. Apparel company Patagonia followed in second place, with furniture company IKEA in third. Other companies in the top 10 include Interface, Natura, Danone, Nestlé, Marks & Spencer, Tesla and BASF. Sector-specific rankings can also be helpful. In Greenpeace's ranking of consumer electronics companies, for example, smartphone company Fairphone was best-in-class, followed by Apple, then Dell and HP.

Increasingly, smartphone apps aim to make it easier for consumers to make informed purchasing decisions. For instance, the Good On You app ranks 2,200 fashion brands to help consumers pick the most sustainable options (see 'There's An App For That' on page 122).

Even without knowledge about the performance of specific companies, consumers can rely on sustainability labels and certification to guide them towards greener products. Environmental charity WWF offers suggestions on what to look for (see 'Follow The Labels' on page 123).

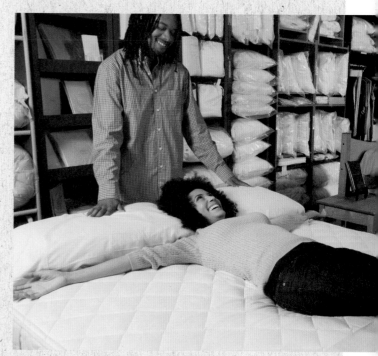

WE'RE ALL ONLY HUMAN

—

Don't beat yourself up if you didn't achieve everything that you set out to achieve. No matter what we do or how eco-friendly we try to be, we will always leave behind a footprint – it's the nature of being alive!

Try not to compare yourself to other people who are on their own eco journeys. What one person finds easy might not be so simple for someone else – it all depends on our personal situations and circumstances. Instead of judging, applaud the steps that others have taken and, if possible, offer encouragement and guidance on any areas that other people are struggling with. We can also take inspiration from what others have achieved.

The journey to becoming more eco-conscious and less impactful is a long one – it's not always easy, but it won't always be hard. Trying to break bad habits and form new, good ones is the key to success. If you make mistakes, don't give up. Acknowledge your mistake, move on and try again! It will take time, patience and learning, but you'll feel great knowing that you're doing your bit to save the world.

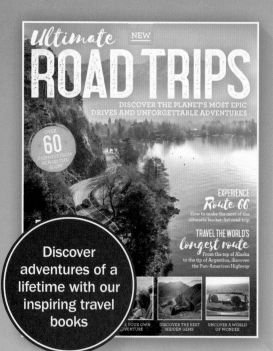

Ultimate *NEW*
ROAD TRIPS
DISCOVER THE PLANET'S MOST EPIC DRIVES AND UNFORGETTABLE ADVENTURES

OVER **60** JOURNEYS FROM ACROSS THE GLOBE

EXPERIENCE
Route 66
How to make the most of the ultimate bucket-list road trip

TRAVEL THE WORLD'S
longest route
From the top of Alaska to the tip of Argentina, discover the Pan-American Highway

Discover adventures of a lifetime with our inspiring travel books

THE BIG BOOK OF
ENGLISH GARDENS

Design ideas • Practical tips • Key plants • Essential directory

101 PLACES TO VISIT BEFORE
JOURNEY THROUGH THE WORLD'S MOST IMPRESSIVE WONDERS

OVER **60** CLASSIC RECIPES
THE GREAT BRITISH
BAKING
BOOK
DISCOVER THE BEST OF BRITISH BAKING

Being Vegan
30+ RECIPES
Dinner party menu ideas

The power of plant protein

Health, beauty & lifestyle

VEGAN ON A BUDGET

NEW

Sleep Better
ULTIMATE COMPANION FOR IMPROVING YOUR SLEEP

INTERACTIVE JOURNAL

Take control of your life and the world around you with our interactive journals

Keto Diet
30 LOW-CARB RECIPES

NEW
Unplug
The Essential Digital Detox Plan

Learn to live MINDFULLY in a digital world

NEW
Sewing Machine
CREATIVE PROJECTS

NEW

Go Plastic Free

AN INTERACTIVE JOURNAL
REDUCE • REUSE • RECYCLE
REPLACE • REFUSE

NEW HEALTH • WELLNESS • HAPPINESS • RELAXATION
The Mindfulness Book

HOW TO REDUCE
STRESS
Essential techniques to strengthen your mind

IMPROVE YOUR
Lifestyle
make physical & mental changes

Inside! HOLISTIC HEALTHCARE

**EXERCISE
NUTRITION
RELATIONSHIPS
ENVIRONMENT**

Get essential advice on how to make positive changes to your health and wellbeing

Recharge
Master THE ART OF CALLIGRAPHY

sleep better

101 *dream* TRAVEL LOCATIONS
JOURNEY THROUGH THE WORLD'S MOST STUNNING DESTINATIONS

NEW

RECIPE
JOURNAL

NEW MORE THAN **150** BODY-SCULPTING EXERCISES
CORE STRENGTH TRAINING BOOK

QUILTING & PATCHWORK
FOR BEGINNERS
Everything you need to know to get started with quilting

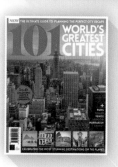

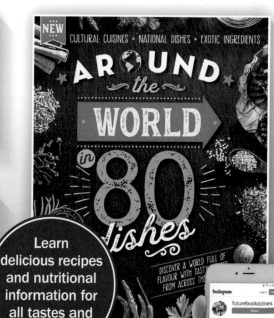

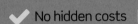 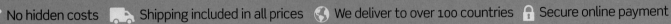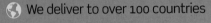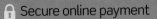